It's another Quality Book from CGP

This book is for anyone doing GCSE Double Science at Higher Level.

Whatever subject you're doing it's the same
old story — there are lots of facts and you've just got
to learn them. KS4 Physics is no different.

Happily this CGP book gives you all that important
information as clearly and concisely as possible.

It's also got some daft bits in to try and make the whole
experience at least vaguely entertaining for you.

What CGP is all about

Our sole aim here at CGP is to produce the highest quality
books — carefully written, immaculately presented and
dangerously close to being funny.

Then we work our socks off to get them out to you
— at the cheapest possible prices.

Contents

Page References for Modular Syllabuses

Published by Coordination Group Publications Ltd.
Updated by   Suzanne Worthington
                      Dominic Hall
                      James Paul Wallis
Illustrations by: Sandy Gardner, e-mail: illustrations@sandygardner.co.uk
                      and Bowser, Colorado USA.

ISBN 1 84146 402 3

Groovy Website: www.cgpbooks.co.uk

Printed by Elanders Hindson, Newcastle upon Tyne.
Clipart sources: CorelDRAW and VECTOR.

Proofreading by:
Deborah Dobson
Iain Nash
James Paul Wallis
With thanks to:
Dr David Stockdale, Durham University for help with page 57.
Photograph on p57 courtesy of NASA   http://nix.nasa.gov

Current, Voltage and Resistance

Isn't electricity great. Mind you it's pretty bad news if the words don't mean anything to you...

1) _CURRENT_ is the flow of electrons round the circuit.
2) _VOLTAGE_ is the driving force that pushes the current round. Kind of like "electrical pressure".
3) _RESISTANCE_ is anything in the circuit which slows the flow down.
4) THERE'S A _BALANCE_: the voltage is trying to push the current round the circuit, and the resistance is opposing it — the relative sizes of the voltage and resistance decide how big the current will be:

> If you increase the _VOLTAGE_ — then _MORE CURRENT_ will flow.
> If you increase the _RESISTANCE_ — then _LESS CURRENT_ will flow.

It's Just Like the Flow of Water Around a Set of Pipes

1) The current is simply like the flow of water.
2) Voltage is like the pressure provided by a pump which pushes the stuff round.
3) Resistance is any sort of constriction in the flow, which is what the pressure has to work against.
4) If you turn up the pump and provide more pressure (or "voltage"), the flow will increase.
5) If you put in more constrictions ("resistance"), the flow (current) will decrease.

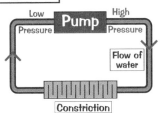

In Metals the Current is Carried by Electrons

1) Electric current will only flow if there are charges which can move freely.
2) Metals contain a "sea" of free electrons (which are negatively charged) and which flow throughout the metal.
3) This is what allows electric current to flow so well in all metals.

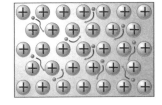

But Electrons Flow the Opposite Way to Conventional Current

We normally say that current in a circuit flows from positive to negative. Alas, electrons were discovered long after that was decided and they turned out to be negatively charged — unlucky. This means they actually flow from −ve to +ve, opposite to the flow of "conventional current".

In Electrolytes, Current is Carried by Both +ve and −ve Charges

1) Electrolytes are liquids which contain charges which can move freely.
2) They are either ions dissolved in water, like salt solution, or molten ionic liquids, like molten sodium chloride.
3) When a voltage is applied the positive charges move towards the −ve, and the negative charges move towards the +ve. This is an electric current.

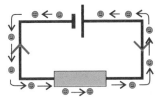

AC Changes Direction but DC Doesn't

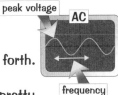

Direct current keeps flowing in the same direction all the time. The CRO trace is a horizontal line.

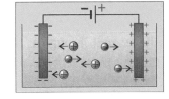

Alternating current keeps reversing its direction back and forth. The CRO trace is always a wave.
You need to learn these CRO traces — I've not put them in cos they're pretty.

Understanding currents — easy as pie...

This page is all about electric current — what it is, what makes it move, and what tries to stop it. This is the most basic stuff on electricity there is. You realise that you'll never be able to learn anything else about electricity until you know this stuff — don't you? Just checking.

The Standard Test Circuit

This is without doubt the most totally bog-standard circuit the world has ever known. So know it.

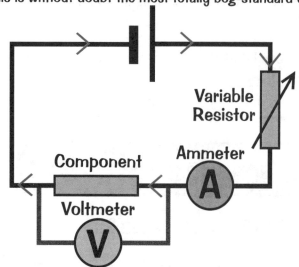

Variable Resistor

Component

Ammeter

Voltmeter

The Ammeter

1) Measures the <u>current</u> (in <u>Amps</u>) flowing through the component.
2) Must be placed <u>in series</u>.
3) Can be put <u>anywhere</u> in series in the <u>main circuit</u>, but <u>never in parallel</u> like the voltmeter.

The Voltmeter

1) Measures the <u>voltage</u> (in <u>Volts</u>) across the component.
2) Must be placed <u>in parallel</u> around the <u>component under test</u> — <u>NOT</u> around the variable resistor or the battery!
3) The <u>proper</u> name for "<u>voltage</u>" is "<u>potential difference</u>" or "<u>p.d.</u>"

Five Important Points

1) This <u>very basic circuit</u> is used for <u>testing components</u>, and for getting <u>V-I graphs</u> for them.
2) The <u>component</u>, the <u>ammeter</u> and the <u>variable resistor</u> are all <u>in series</u>, which means they can be put <u>in any order</u> in the main circuit. The <u>voltmeter</u>, on the other hand, can only be placed <u>in parallel</u> around the <u>component under test</u>, as shown. Anywhere else is a definite <u>no-no</u>.
3) As you <u>vary</u> the <u>variable resistor</u> it alters the <u>current</u> flowing through the circuit.
4) This allows you to take several <u>pairs of readings</u> from the <u>ammeter</u> and <u>voltmeter</u>.
5) You can then <u>plot</u> these values for <u>current</u> and <u>voltage</u> on a <u>V-I graph</u>, like the ones below.

Four Hideously Important Voltage-Current Graphs

V-I graphs show how the current varies as you change the voltage. Learn these four real well:

Resistor

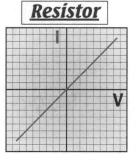

The current through a <u>resistor</u> (at constant temperature) is <u>proportional to voltage</u>.

Different Wires

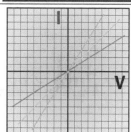

<u>Different wires</u> have different <u>resistances</u>, hence the different <u>slopes</u>.

Filament Lamp

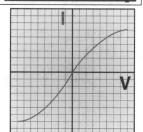

As the <u>temperature</u> of the filament <u>increases</u>, the <u>resistance increases</u>, hence the <u>curve</u>.

Diode

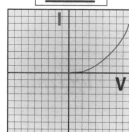

Current will only flow through a diode <u>in one direction</u>, as shown.

Calculating Resistance: R =V/I, (or R ="1/gradient")

For the <u>straight-line graphs</u> the resistance of the component is <u>steady</u> and is equal to the <u>inverse</u> of the <u>gradient</u> of the line, or "<u>1/gradient</u>". In other words, the <u>steeper</u> the graph, the <u>lower</u> the resistance. If the graph <u>curves</u>, it means the resistance is <u>changing</u>. In that case R can be found for any point by taking the <u>pair of values</u> (V,I) from the graph and sticking them in the formula <u>R =V/I</u> (See P.8). Easy.

In the end, you'll have to learn this — resistance is futile...

There are quite a lot of important details on this page and you need to <u>learn all of them</u>. The only way to make sure you really know it is to <u>cover up the page</u> and see how much of it you can <u>scribble down</u> from <u>memory</u>. Sure, it's not that easy — but it's the only way. Enjoy.

Circuit Symbols and Devices

You have to know <u>all</u> these circuit symbols for the Exam.

Circuit Symbols You Should Know:

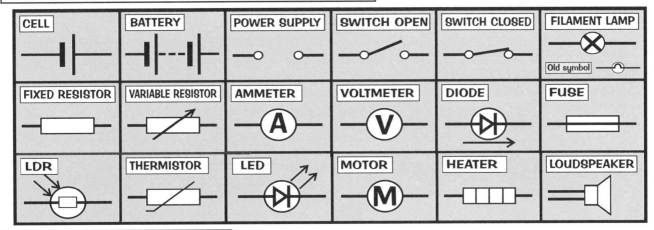

CELL	BATTERY	POWER SUPPLY	SWITCH OPEN	SWITCH CLOSED	FILAMENT LAMP (Old symbol)
FIXED RESISTOR	VARIABLE RESISTOR	AMMETER	VOLTMETER	DIODE	FUSE
LDR	THERMISTOR	LED	MOTOR	HEATER	LOUDSPEAKER

1) Variable Resistor

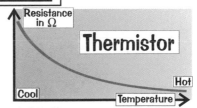

1) A <u>resistor</u> whose resistance can be <u>changed</u> by twiddling a knob or something.
2) The old-fashioned ones are <u>huge coils of wire</u> with a <u>slider</u> on them.
3) They're great for <u>altering the current</u> flowing through a circuit.
   Turn the resistance <u>up</u>, the current <u>drops</u>. Turn the resistance <u>down</u>, the current goes <u>up</u>.

2) "Semiconductor Diode" or just "Diode"

A special device made from <u>semiconductor</u> material such as <u>silicon</u>. It lets current
flow freely through it <u>in one direction</u>, but <u>not</u> in the other (i.e. there's a very high resistance
in the <u>reverse</u> direction).   This turns out to be real useful in various <u>electronic circuits</u>.

3) Light Emitting Diode or "LED" to you

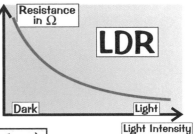

1) A diode which <u>gives out light</u>. It only lets current go through in <u>one direction</u>.
2) When it does pass current, it gives out a pretty <u>red</u> or <u>green</u> or <u>yellow</u> light.
3) Stereos usually have lots of jolly little LEDs which <u>light up</u> as the music's playing.

4) Light Dependent Resistor or "LDR" to you

1) In <u>bright light</u>, the resistance <u>falls</u>.
2) In <u>darkness</u>, the resistance is <u>highest</u>.
3) This makes it a useful device for various <u>electronic
   circuits</u> eg.. <u>automatic night lights</u>; <u>burglar detectors</u>.

5) Thermistor (Temperature-dependent Resistor)

1) In <u>hot</u> conditions, the resistance <u>drops</u>.
2) In <u>cool</u> conditions, the resistance goes <u>up</u>.
3) Thermistors make useful <u>temperature detectors</u>.
   eg.. <u>car engine</u> temperature sensors and
   electronic <u>thermostats</u> for central heating.

"Diode" — wasn't that a film starring Bruce Willis...

Another page of basic but important details about electrical circuits. You need to know all those
circuit symbols as well as the extra details for the five special devices.   When you think you
know it all try <u>covering the page</u> and <u>scribbling it all down</u>. See how you did, and <u>then try again</u>.

Series Circuits

You need to be able to tell the difference between series and parallel circuits <u>just by looking at them</u>. You also need to know the <u>rules</u> about what happens with both types. Read on.

Series Circuits — all or nothing

1) In <u>series circuits</u>, the different components are connected <u>in a line</u>, <u>end to end</u>, between the +ve and –ve of the power supply (except for <u>voltmeters</u>, which are always connected <u>in parallel</u>, but they don't count as part of the circuit).
2) If you remove or disconnect <u>one</u> component, the circuit is <u>broken</u> and they all <u>stop</u>.
3) This is generally <u>not very handy</u>, and in practice, <u>very few things</u> are connected in series.

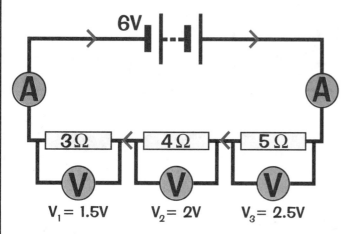

Voltages add to equal the <u>supply</u>: 1.5 + 2+ 2.5 = 6V
<u>Total resistance</u> = 3 + 4 + 5 = 12 Ohms
<u>Current</u> =V/R = 6 / 12 = 0.5 A

In Series Circuits:

1) The <u>total resistance</u> is just the <u>sum</u> of all the resistances.
2) The <u>same current</u> flows through <u>all parts</u> of the circuit.
3) The <u>size of the current</u> is determined by the <u>total p.d. of the cells</u> and the <u>total resistance</u> of the circuit: i.e. I = V/R
4) The <u>total p.d.</u> of the <u>supply</u> is <u>shared</u> between the various <u>components</u>, so the <u>voltages</u> round a series circuit <u>always add up</u> to equal the <u>total voltage</u> of the supply.
5) The <u>bigger</u> the <u>resistance</u> of a component, the bigger its <u>share</u> of the <u>total p.d.</u>

Total p.d., Voltmeters and Ammeters

1) The <u>total p.d.</u> provided by cells in <u>series</u> is the <u>sum</u> of the individual p.ds.
2) <u>Voltmeters</u> are always connected <u>in parallel</u> around components. In a <u>series circuit</u>, you can put voltmeters <u>around each component</u>. The readings from all the components will <u>add up</u> to equal the reading from the <u>voltage source</u> (the cells). Simple.
3) <u>Ammeters</u> can be placed <u>anywhere</u> in a <u>series circuit</u> and will <u>all give the same reading</u>.

Christmas Fairy Lights are Wired in Series

<u>Christmas fairy lights</u> are about the <u>only real-life example</u> of things connected in <u>series</u>, and we all know what a <u>pain</u> they are when the <u>whole lot go out</u> just because <u>one</u> of the bulbs is slightly dodgy.

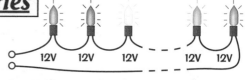

The only <u>advantage</u> is that the bulbs can be <u>very small</u> because the total 230V is <u>shared out between</u> <u>them</u>, so <u>each bulb</u> only has a <u>small voltage</u> across it.

<u>By contrast</u>, a string of lights as used on a <u>building site</u> are connected in <u>parallel</u> so that each bulb receives the <u>full 230V</u>. If <u>one</u> is removed, <u>the rest stay lit</u>. Which is most <u>convenient</u>.

Make sure you know the <u>difference</u> between these two wiring diagrams.

Series Circuits — phew, it's just one thing after another...

They really do want you to know the difference between series and parallel circuits. It's not that tricky but you do have to make a real effort to <u>learn all the details</u>. That's what this page is for. Learn all those details, then <u>cover the page</u> and <u>scribble them all down</u>. Then try again...

Parallel Circuits

Parallel circuits are much more <u>sensible</u> than series circuits and so they're <u>much more common</u> in <u>real life</u>.

Parallel Circuits — Independence and Isolation

1) In <u>parallel circuits</u>, each component is <u>separately connected</u> to the +ve and −ve of the <u>supply</u>.
2) If you remove or disconnect <u>one</u> of them, it will <u>hardly affect the others at all</u>.
3) This is <u>obviously</u> how <u>most things</u> must be connected, for example in <u>cars</u> and in <u>household electrics</u>. You have to be able to switch everything on and off <u>separately</u>.

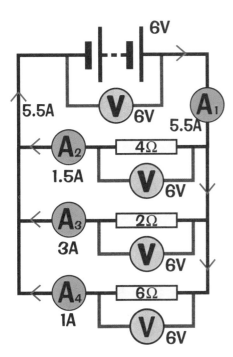

In Parallel Circuits:

1) <u>All components</u> get the <u>full source p.d.</u>, so the voltage is the <u>same</u> across all components.

2) The <u>current</u> through each component <u>depends on its resistance</u>.
The <u>lower</u> the resistance, the <u>bigger</u> the current that'll flow through it.

3) The <u>total current</u> flowing around the circuit is equal to the <u>total</u> of all the currents in the <u>separate branches</u>.

4) In a parallel circuit, there are <u>junctions</u> where the current either <u>splits</u> or <u>rejoins</u>. The total current going <u>into</u> a junction <u>always equals</u> the total currents <u>leaving</u> — fairly obviously.

5) The <u>total resistance</u> of the circuit is <u>tricky to work out</u>, but it's <u>always less</u> than the branch with the smallest resistance.

<u>Voltages</u> all equal to <u>supply voltage</u>: = 6V
<u>Total R</u> is <u>less than</u> the <u>smallest</u>, i.e. <u>less than</u> 2 Ω
<u>Total Current</u> (A_1) = <u>sum</u> of all branches = $A_2 + A_3 + A_4$

Connection of Voltmeters and Ammeters

1) Once again the <u>voltmeters</u> are always connected <u>in parallel</u> around components.

2) <u>Ammeters</u> can be placed <u>in each branch</u> to measure the <u>different currents</u> flowing through each branch, as well as <u>one near the supply</u> to measure the <u>total current</u> flowing out of it.

Everything Electrical in a Car is Connected in Parallel

<u>Parallel connection</u> is <u>essential</u> in a car to give these <u>two features</u>:

> 1) Everything can be <u>turned on and off separately</u>.
> 2) Everything always gets the <u>full voltage</u> from the battery.

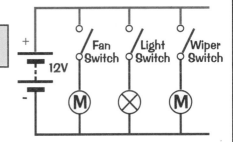

The only <u>slight effect</u> is that when you turn <u>lots of things on</u> the lights may go <u>dim</u> because the battery can't provide <u>full voltage</u> under <u>heavy load</u>. This is normally a <u>very slight</u> effect. You can spot the same thing at home when you turn a kettle on, if you watch very carefully.

Electric Circuits — unparalleled dreariness...

Make sure you can scribble down a parallel circuit and know what the advantages are. Learn the five numbered points and the details for connecting ammeters and voltmeters, and also what two features make parallel connection essential in a car. Then <u>cover the page</u> and <u>scribble it</u>...

Static Electricity

Static electricity is all about charges which are <u>not</u> free to move. This causes them to build up in one place and it often ends with a <u>spark</u> or a <u>shock</u> when they do finally move.

1) Build up of Static is Caused by Friction

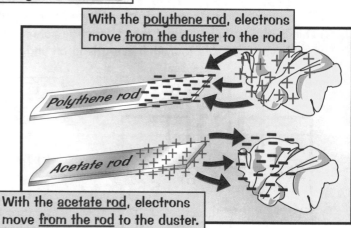

With the <u>polythene rod</u>, electrons move <u>from the duster</u> to the rod.

1) When two <u>insulating</u> materials are <u>rubbed together</u>, electrons will be <u>scraped off one</u> and <u>dumped on the other</u>.

2) This'll leave a <u>positive static charge</u> on one and a <u>negative</u> static charge on the other.

3) <u>Which way</u> the electrons are transferred <u>depends</u> on the <u>two materials</u> involved.

4) The classic examples are <u>polythene</u> and <u>acetate</u> rods being rubbed with a <u>cloth duster</u>, as shown in the diagrams:

With the <u>acetate rod</u>, electrons move <u>from the rod</u> to the duster.

2) Only Electrons Move — Never the Positive Charges

<u>Watch out for this in Exams</u>. Both +ve and –ve electrostatic charges are only ever produced by the <u>movement of electrons</u>. The positive charges <u>definitely do not move</u>! A positive static charge is always caused by electrons <u>moving away elsewhere</u>, as shown above. Don't forget!

3) Like Charges Repel, Opposite Charges Attract

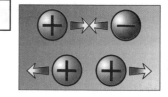

This is <u>easy</u> and, I'd have thought, <u>kind of obvious</u>.
Two things with <u>opposite electric charges</u> are <u>attracted</u> to each other.
Two things with the <u>same electric charge</u> will <u>repel</u> each other.
These <u>forces get weaker</u> the <u>further apart</u> the two things are — pretty obviously.

4) Charging by Induction is a bit Tricky

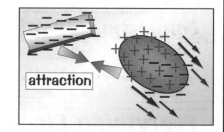

When something which is <u>charged</u> comes near something <u>which isn't</u>, it tends to <u>induce charge</u>, because electrons in the <u>uncharged</u> object <u>move towards or away</u> from the charged object.
The <u>result</u> is always the same — the new arrangement of charge always makes the two objects <u>pull together</u> because the <u>repelling charges</u> are now <u>further apart</u> than the <u>attracting charges</u>.
It's <u>tricky</u>, but you <u>can</u> understand it — and you <u>can</u> learn it.

attraction

5) As Charge Builds Up, So Does the Voltage — Causing Sparks

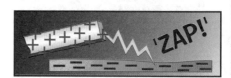

The <u>greater the charge</u> on an <u>isolated</u> object, the <u>greater the voltage</u> between it and the Earth. If the voltage gets <u>big enough</u> there's a <u>spark</u> which <u>jumps across</u> the gap. High voltage cables can be <u>dangerous</u> for this reason. Big sparks have been known to <u>leap</u> from <u>overhead cables</u> to earth. But not often.

'ZAP!'

A charged conductor can be <u>discharged safely</u> by connecting it to earth with a <u>metal strap</u>.

Phew — it's enough to make your hair stand on end...

The way to tackle this page is to first <u>learn the five headings</u> till you can <u>scribble them all down</u>. Then learn the details for each one, and keep practising by <u>covering the page</u> and scribbling down each heading with as many details as you can remember for each one. Just <u>keep trying</u>...

Static Electricity — Examples

They like asking you to give *quite detailed examples* in Exams. Make sure you *learn all these details*.

Static Electricity Being Helpful:

1) Inkjet Printer:

1) Tiny droplets of ink are forced out of a *fine nozzle*, making them *electrically charged*.
2) The droplets are *deflected* as they pass between two metal plates. A *voltage* is applied to the plates — one is *negative* and the other is *positive*.
3) The droplets are *attracted* to the plate of the *opposite* charge and *repelled* from the plate with the *same* charge.

jet of ink

charged plates

printout

4) The *size* and *direction* of the voltage across each plate changes so each droplet is deflected to hit a *different place* on the paper.
5) Loads of tiny dots make up your printout. Clever.

2) Photocopier:

1) The *metal plate* is electrically charged. An image of what you're copying is projected onto it.
2) Whiter bits of the thing you're copying make *light* fall on the plate and the charge *leaks away*.

light

-ve

heated rollers

toner (black powder) attracted to plate

3) The charged bits attract *black powder*, which is transferred onto paper.
4) The paper is *heated* so the powder sticks.
5) Voilà, a photocopy of your piece of paper (or whatever else you've shoved in there).

3) Spray Painting and Dust Removal in Chimneys...

These are other uses but photocopiers and inkjet printers are what they *really* want you to learn.

Static Electricity Being a Little Joker:

1) Car Shocks

Air rushing past your car can give it a +ve charge. When you get out and touch the door it gives you a real buzz — in the Exam make sure you say "electrons flow from earth, through you, to neutralise the +ve charge on the car." Some cars have conducting rubber strips which hang down behind the car. This gives a safe discharge to earth, but spoils all the fun.

2) Clothing Crackles

When synthetic clothes are dragged over each other (like in a tumble drier) or over your head, electrons get scraped off, leaving static charges on both parts, and that leads to the inevitable — attraction (they stick together) and little sparks / shocks as the charges rearrange themselves.

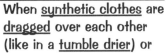

Static Electricity Playing at Terrorist:

1) Lightning

Rain droplets fall to Earth with positive charge. This creates a huge voltage and a big spark.

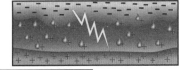

2) Grain Chutes, Paper Rollers and The Fuel Filling Nightmare:

1) As fuel flows out of a filler pipe, or paper drags over rollers, or grain shoots out of pipes, then static can build up.
2) This can easily lead to a spark and in dusty or fumey places — BOOM!
3) The solution: make the nozzles or rollers out of metal so that the charge is conducted away, instead of building up.
4) It's also good to have earthing straps between the fuel tank and the fuel pipe.

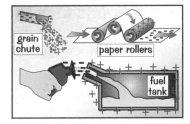

grain chute

paper rollers

fuel tank

Static Electricity — learn the shocking truth...

You really need to learn those two big examples at the top. All the exam boards mention photocopiers and inkjet printers so I bet there'll be a question on them. Crumbs, it's almost relevant to real-life too. Learn the numbered points and keep scribbling them down to check.

Symbols, Units and Formulas

This is all very basic stuff and you need to learn it all pretty thoroughly. If you don't, and you then try and do other Physics, it's like trying to write stories without learning the alphabet first. So as long as this is all just a load of weird symbols and nonsense to you then you won't find Physics very easy at all. This is the Physics alphabet and without it you're... in trouble.

	Quantity	Symbol	Standard Units	Formula
1	Potential Difference	V	Volts, V	$V = I \times R$
2	Current	I	Amperes, A	$I = V / R$
3	Resistance	R	Ohms, Ω	$R = V / I$
4	Charge	Q	Coulombs, C	$Q = I \times t$
5	Power	P	Watts, W	$P = V \times I$ or $P = I^2 R$
6	Energy	E	Joules, J	$E = QV$ or $V = E/Q$
7	Time	t	Seconds, s	$E = P \times t$ or $E = IVt$
8	Force	F	Newtons, N	$F = ma$
9	Mass	m	Kilograms, kg	
10	Weight (a force)	W	Newtons, N	$W = mg$
11	Density	D	kg per m^3, kg/m^3	$D = m/V$
12	Moment	M	Newton-metres, Nm	$M = F \times r$
13	Velocity or Speed	v or s	metres/sec, m/s	$s = d/t$
14	Acceleration	a	metres/sec^2, m/s^2	$a = \Delta v/t$ or $a = F/m$
15	Pressure	P	Pascals, Pa (N/m^2)	$P = F/A$
16	Area	A	metres^2, m^2	
17	Volume	V	metres^3, m^3	$P_1 V_1 = P_2 V_2$
18	Frequency	f	Hertz, Hz	$f = 1/T$ (T=time period)
19	Wavelength (a distance)	λ or d	metres, m	$v = f \times \lambda$ (wave formula)
20	Work done	Wd	Joules, J	$Wd = F \times d$
21	Power	P	Watts, W	$P = Wd / t$
22	Potential Energy	PE	Joules, J	$PE = m \times g \times h$
23	Kinetic Energy	KE	Joules, J	$KE = \frac{1}{2}mv^2$

There's also <u>efficiency</u>, which has no units:

Efficiency = $\dfrac{\text{Useful work output}}{\text{Total energy input}}$

And also the <u>transformer equation</u>:

$\dfrac{\text{Primary Coil Voltage}}{\text{Secondary Voltage}} = \dfrac{\text{No. of turns on Primary Coil}}{\text{No. of turns on Secondary}}$

Physics — isn't it just wonderful...

Your task is <u>simplicity itself</u>. Leave the "Quantity" column exposed and cover up the other three. Then simply <u>fill in the three columns</u> for each quantity: "Symbol", "Units", "Formula". And just keep practising and practising till you can <u>do it all</u>. This really is so important. So do it.

Using Formulas

Always the Same Old Routine

The thing about using formulas in Physics is that it's <u>always the same old routine</u>. Once you've learnt how to do it for <u>one</u> formula, you can do it for <u>any other</u>. And that makes the whole thing <u>really simple</u> — but there's still a lot of people out there who seem to make a real meal of it. Let's take it nice and slowly...

Formula Triangles are Pretty Useful for Getting it Right

<u>All</u> the formulas on the opposite page (except "$P_1V_1=P_2V_2$") can be put into <u>formula triangles</u>.
It's <u>pretty important</u> to learn how to put any formula into a triangle. There are <u>two easy rules</u>:

1) If the formula is "<u>A = B×C</u>" then <u>A goes on the top</u> and <u>B×C goes on the bottom</u>.
2) If the formula is "<u>A = B/C</u>" then <u>B must go on the top</u> (because that's the only way it'll give "B divided by something") — and so pretty obviously <u>A and C must go on the bottom</u>.

Three Examples:

$V=I\times R$
turns into:

$P=I^2\times R$
turns into:

$V=E/Q$
turns into:

<u>How to use them:</u> Cover up the thing you want to find and write down what's left showing.
<u>EXAMPLE:</u> To find Q from the last one, cover up Q and you get E/V left showing, so "Q = E/V"

Using Formulas — The Three Rules

1) <u>Find a formula</u> which contains <u>the thing you want to find</u> together with the <u>other things</u> which you've got <u>values</u> for. Convert that formula into a formula triangle.
2) <u>Stick</u> the numbers in and <u>work out</u> the answer.
3) <u>Think very carefully</u> about all the <u>units</u> — and check that the answer is <u>sensible</u>.

<u>EXAMPLE</u>: *A hairdrier is rated at 700 W and draws a current of 3 A Find its resistance.*
<u>ANSWER</u>: *The three quantities mentioned are <u>power</u> (700 W), <u>current</u> (3 A) and <u>resistance</u>.*
 1) The formula with these three in is "$P = I^2R$", and the formula triangle version gives us $R = P / I^2$
 2) Sticking the numbers in: $R = 700/3^2 = 700/9 = 77.78 = 78\ \Omega$
 3) The power and current are already in their proper units of Watts and Amps, so that's OK.
  The answer for R must be given in its proper units too, namely Ω, which we've done.
  The value of 78 W is fine. If it was 1,000,000 W or 0.00034 W you'd worry and check it.

Watch out For the Units

Once you've got the hang of formula triangles there's only one thing left to get wrong — <u>units</u>.
There's <u>two things</u> about units that you have to really watch out for:

1) Make sure that the numbers <u>you put in</u> to the formula are in <u>standard (SI) units</u>.
2) When you write the answer down, make sure your <u>answer</u> has its <u>proper units</u>.

<u>IMPORTANT EXAMPLES:</u> 500 g must be turned into 0.5 kg, 2 minutes into 120 seconds, 700 kJ into 700,000 J, 145 cm into 1.45 m, etc. before putting them into a formula. If you don't put SI units <u>in</u> then the answer won't come <u>out</u> with SI units, which can get tricky unless you know what you're doing.

Formulas — aren't they just fabulous...

Physics formulas are <u>amazingly repetitive</u>. You really must get it into your head that they're basically <u>all the same</u>. This page has the <u>simple rules</u> that would allow <u>anyone</u> to work out the answers without really knowing anything about Physics at all. It's easy peasy, surely it is.

Energy in Circuits

You can look at electrical circuits in two ways. The first is in terms of a voltage pushing the current round and the resistances opposing the flow, as on P.1. The other way of looking at circuits is in terms of energy transfer. Learn them both and be ready to tackle questions about either.

Energy is Transferred from Cells and Other Sources

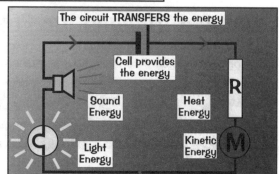

The circuit TRANSFERS the energy

Cell provides the energy

Sound Energy

Heat Energy

Light Energy

Kinetic Energy

1) Anything which supplies electricity is also supplying energy. There are four sources you need to learn:
   CELLS, BATTERIES, GENERATORS and SOLAR CELLS.

2) The energy is transferred by the electric circuit to components such as lamps, resistors, bells, motors, LEDs, buzzers, etc.

3) These components perform their own energy transfer and convert the electrical energy in the circuit into other forms of energy: HEAT, LIGHT, SOUND or MOVEMENT.

4) Don't forget that a complete circuit is needed for the current to flow. If the circuit is broken there will be no current flow and no transfer of energy.

Electricity Can produce Four Effects: Learn these as specific examples:

| HEAT: Hairdriers/kettles | LIGHT: light bulbs | SOUND: speakers | MOTION: motors |

All Resistors produce Heat when a Current flows through them

Heater coil

1) This is important. Whenever a current flows through anything with electrical resistance (which is pretty well everything) then electrical energy is converted into heat energy.
2) The more current that flows, the more heat is produced.
3) Also, a bigger voltage means more heating, because it pushes more current through.
4) However, the higher you make the resistance, the less heat is produced. This is because a higher resistance means less current will flow, and that reduces the heating.
5) The amount of heat produced can be measured by putting a resistor in a known amount of water or inside a solid block and measuring the increase in temperature.

Charge, Voltage and Energy Change

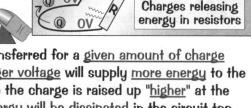

Charges gaining energy at the battery

+6V

+6V

+3V

0V

0V

Charges releasing energy in resistors

1) When electrical charge (Q) goes through a change in voltage (V), then energy (E) is transferred.
2) Energy is supplied to the charge at the power source to raise it through a voltage.
3) The charge gives up this energy when it falls through any voltage drop in components elsewhere in the circuit.
4) The formula is really simple: $E = QV$

$$\frac{E}{Q \times V}$$

The bigger the change in voltage (or p.d.), the more energy is transferred for a given amount of charge passing through the circuit. That means that a battery with a bigger voltage will supply more energy to the circuit for every coulomb of charge which flows round it, because the charge is raised up "higher" at the start (see above diagram) — and as the diagram shows, more energy will be dissipated in the circuit too. This gives rise to two definitions which I guess you should learn, although they're seriously dull:

> 1) ONE VOLT is ONE JOULE PER COULOMB
> 2) VOLTAGE is the ENERGY TRANSFERRED PER UNIT CHARGE passed

Electricity — why does it all turn out so dreary ...

I try to make it interesting, really I do. I mean, underneath it all, electricity is pretty good stuff, but somehow every page just seems to end up stuffed full of interminably dreary facts. Well look, *I tried*, OK. It's still dreary but you've just gotta learn it all, and that's that.

The Cost of Domestic Electricity

Electricity is by far the most useful form of energy. Compared to gas or oil or coal etc. it's much easier to turn it into the four main types of useful energy: Heat, light, sound and motion.

Reading Your Electricity Meter and Working out the Bill

Yip, this is in the syllabus. Don't ask me why, because you never actually need to bother in real life.

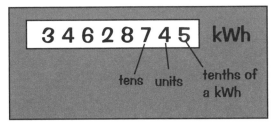

tens units tenths of a kWh

The reading on your meter shows the total number of units (kWh) used since the meter was fitted. Each bill is worked out from the increase in the meter reading since it was last read for the previous bill.
You need to study this bill until you know what all the different bits are for, and how it all works out. They could give you one very similar in the Exam.

Electricity Bill

Previous meter reading	345412.3
This meter reading	346287.5
Number of units used	875.2
Cost per unit	6.3p
Cost of electricity used	£55.14p
(875.2 units × 6.3p)	
Fixed Quarterly charge	£7.50
Total Bill	£62.64
VAT @ 8%	£5.01
Final total	£67.65

Kilowatt-hours (kWh) are "UNITS" of Energy

1) Your electricity meter counts the number of "UNITS" used.
2) A "UNIT" is otherwise known as a kilowatt-hour, or kWh.
3) A "kWh" might sound like a unit of power, but it's not — it's an amount of energy.

> A **KILOWATT-HOUR** is the amount of electrical energy used by a **1 kW appliance** left on for **1 HOUR**.

4) Make sure you can turn 1 kWh into 3,600,000 Joules like this:
"E=P×t" = 1kW × 1 hour = 1000W × 3,600 secs = 3,600,000 J   (=3.6 MJ)
(The formula is "Energy = Power×time", and the units must be converted to SI first. See P.8 and P.9)

The Two Easy Formulae for Calculating The Cost of Electricity

These must surely be the two most trivial and obvious formulas you'll ever see:

No. of **UNITS** (kWh) used = **POWER** (in kW) × **TIME** (in hours)	Units = kW × hours
COST = No. of **UNITS** × **PRICE** per UNIT	Cost = Units × Price

EXAMPLE: *Find the cost of leaving a 60 W light bulb on for a) 30 minutes   b) one year.*
ANSWER: a) No. of Units = kW × hours = 0.06kW × ½hr = 0.03 units.
    Cost = Units × price per unit(6.3p) = 0.03 × 6.3p = 0.189p for 30 mins.

    b) No. of Units = kW × hours = 0.06kW × (24×365)hr = 525.6 units.
    Cost = Units × price per unit(6.3p) = 525.6 × 6.3p = £33.11 for one year.

N.B. Always turn the power into kW (not Watts) and the time into hours (not minutes)

Kilowa Towers — the Best Lit Hotel in Hawaii...

This page has three sections and you need to learn the stuff in all of them. Start by memorising the headings, then learn the details under each heading. Then cover the page and scribble down what you know. Check back and see what you missed, and then try again. And keep trying.

Mains Electricity — Plugs and Fuses

Now then, did you know... electricity is dangerous. It can kill you. Well just watch out for it, that's all.

Hazards in The Home — Eliminate Them before They Eliminate You

A likely Exam question will show you a picture of domestic bliss but with various electrical hazards in the picture such as kids shoving their fingers into sockets and stuff like that, and they'll ask you to list all the hazards. This should be mostly common sense, but it won't half help if you've already learnt this list:

1) Long cables or frayed cables.
2) Cables in contact with something hot or wet.
3) Pet rabbits or children (always hazardous).
4) Water near sockets, or shoving things into sockets.
5) Damaged plugs, or too many plugs into one socket.
6) Lighting sockets without bulbs in.
7) Appliances without their covers on.

Plugs and Cables — Learn the Safety Features

Get the Wiring Right:

1) The right coloured wire is connected to each pin, and firmly screwed in.

2) No bare wires showing inside the plug.

3) Cable grip tightly fastened over the cable outer layer.

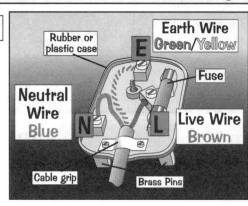

Earth Wire Green/Yellow

Rubber or plastic case

E

Fuse

Neutral Wire Blue

N   L

Live Wire Brown

Cable grip

Brass Pins

Plug Features:

1) The metal parts are made of copper or brass because these are very good conductors.

2) The case, cable grip and cable insulation are all made of plastic because this is a really good insulator and is flexible too.

3) This all keeps the electricity flowing where it should.

Earthing and Fuses Prevent Fires and Shocks

The LIVE WIRE alternates between a HIGH +VE AND −VE VOLTAGE, with an average of about 230V. The NEUTRAL WIRE is always at 0 V Electricity normally flows in and out through the live and neutral wires only. The EARTH WIRE and fuse (or circuit breaker) are just for safety and work together like this:

1) If a fault develops in which the live somehow touches the metal case, then because the case is earthed, a big current flows in through the live, through the case and out down the earth wire.

2) This surge in current blows the fuse (or trips the circuit breaker), which cuts off the live supply.

3) This isolates the whole appliance making it impossible to get an electric shock from the case. It also prevents the risk of fire caused by the heating effect of a large current.

4) Fuses should be rated as near as possible but just higher than the normal operating current (See P. 13).

TOASTER   heater coil

Big current surges to earth

Big current now flows out through earth

Fault Allows live to touch metal case

Big surge in current blows fuse......

....which isolates the appliance from the live

POP

Safe

All appliances with metal cases must be "earthed" to avoid the danger of electric shock.
"Earthing" just means the metal case must be attached to the earth wire in the cable.
If the appliance has a plastic casing and no metal parts showing then it's said to be double insulated.
Anything with double insulation like that doesn't need an earth wire, just a live and neutral.

Some people are so careless with electricity — it's shocking...

Make sure you can list all those hazards in the home. Make sure you know all the details for wiring a plug. Trickiest of all, make sure you understand how earthing and fuses act together to make things safe. Learnt it all? Good-O. So cover the page and scribble it all down again.

The National Grid

1) The National Grid is the network of pylons and cables which covers the whole country.
2) It takes electricity from the power stations, to just where it's needed in homes and industry.
3) It enables power to be generated anywhere on the grid, and to then be supplied anywhere else on the grid.

All Power Stations are Pretty Much the Same

They all have a boiler of some sort, which makes steam which drives a turbine which drives a generator.
The generator produces electricity (by induction) by rotating an electromagnet within coils of wire (see P. 18).

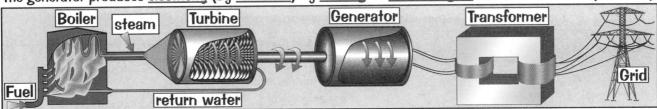

Learn all these features of the NATIONAL GRID — power stations, transformers, pylons, etc:

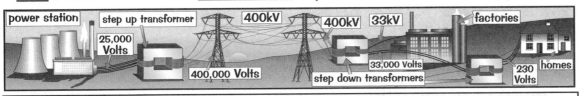

Pylon Cables are at 400,000 V to keep the Current Low

You need to understand why the voltage is so high and why it's AC. Learn these points:
1) The formula for power supplied is: Power = Voltage × Current or: $P = V \times I$
2) So to transmit a lot of power, you either need high voltage or high current.
3) The problem with high current is the loss (as heat) due to the resistance of the cables.
4) The formula for power loss due to resistance in the cables is: $P = I^2R$.
5) Because of the I^2 bit, if the current is 10 times bigger, the losses will be 100 times bigger.
6) It's much cheaper to boost the voltage up to 400,000 V and keep the current very low.
7) This requires transformers as well as big pylons with huge insulators, but it's still cheaper.
8) The transformers have to step the voltage up at one end, for efficient transmission, and then bring it back down to safe useable levels at the other end.
9) This is why it has to be AC on the National Grid — so that the transformers will work!
10) Mains electricity in your house is AC 50 Hz — the voltage changes direction 100 times a second.

Calculating Electrical Power and Fuse Ratings

1) The standard formula for electrical power is: $\qquad$ P=VI
2) If you combine it with $V=I \times R$, and replace the "V" with "I×R", you get: $\qquad$ P=I²R
3) If instead you use $V=I \times R$ and replace the "I" with "V/R", you get: $\qquad$ P=V²/R
4) You choose which one of these formulas to use, purely and simply by seeing which one contains the three quantities which are involved in the problem you're looking at.

Calculating Fuse Ratings — Always Use the Formula: "P=VI"

Most electrical goods indicate their power rating and voltage rating. To work out the fuse needed, you need to work out the current that the item will normally use. That means using "P=VI", or rather, "I=P/V".
EXAMPLE: *A hairdrier is rated at 240V, 1.1 kW. Find the fuse needed.*
ANSWER: *I = P/V = 1100/240 = 4.6 A. Normally, the fuse should be rated just a little higher than the normal current, so a 5 amp fuse is ideal for this one.*

400,000 Volts? — that could give you a buzz...

Quite a few tricky details on this page. The power station and National Grid are easy enough, but fully explaining why pylon cables are at 400,000 V is a bit trickier — but you do need to learn it. The same goes for the power formulae and working out fuse ratings. Scribble it.

Magnetic Fields

There's a proper definition of a <u>magnetic field</u> which you really ought to learn:

> A _MAGNETIC FIELD_ is a region where _MAGNETIC MATERIALS_ (like iron and steel)
> and also _WIRES CARRYING CURRENTS_ experience _A FORCE_ acting on them.

Learn all These Magnetic Field Diagrams, Arrow-perfect

They're really likely to give you one of these diagrams to do in your Exam.
So make sure you know them, especially <u>which way the arrows point</u> — <u>always from North to South!</u>

Bar Magnet

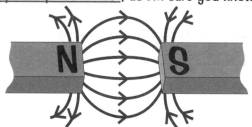

Solenoid

Same field as a bar magnet <u>outside</u>.

<u>Strong and uniform</u> field on the <u>inside</u>.

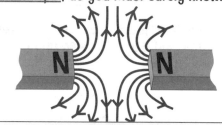

Two Bar Magnets Attracting

<u>Opposite poles attract</u>, as I'm sure you know.

Two Bar Magnets Repelling

<u>Like poles repel</u>, as you must surely know.

The Earth's Magnetic Field

Note that the <u>magnetic poles</u> are <u>opposite</u> to the <u>Geographic Poles</u>, i.e. the <u>south pole</u> is at the <u>North Pole</u> — if you see what I mean!

The Magnetic Field Round a Current-carrying Wire

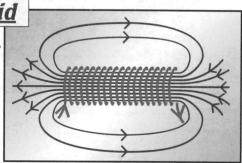

Current

Current

Magnetic Field

The Right Hand Thumb Rule shows which way the magnetic field goes

A Plotting Compass is a Freely Suspended Magnet

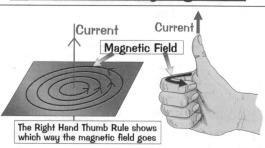

1) This means it always <u>aligns itself</u> with the <u>magnetic field</u> that it's in.
2) This is great for plotting <u>magnetic field lines</u> like around the <u>bar magnets</u> shown above.
3) Away from any magnets, it will <u>align</u> with the magnetic field of the <u>Earth</u> and point <u>North</u>.
4) <u>Any magnet</u> suspended so it can turn <u>freely</u> will also come to rest pointing <u>North-South</u>.
5) The end of the magnet which points North is called a "<u>North-seeking pole</u>" or "<u>magnetic North</u>".
   The end pointing South will therefore be a "<u>magnetic South pole</u>". This is how they got their names.

Magnetic fields — there's no getting away from them...

Mmm, this is a nice easy page for you isn't it. Learn the definition of what a magnetic field is and the six field diagrams. Also learn those five details about plotting compasses and which way the poles are compared to the Earth. Then <u>cover the page</u> and <u>scribble it all down</u>.

Electromagnets

An Electromagnet is just a Coil of Wire with an Iron Core

1) Electromagnets are really simple.

2) They're simply a solenoid (which is just a coil of wire) with a piece of "soft" iron inside.

3) When current flows through the wires of the solenoid it creates a magnetic field around it.

4) The soft iron core has the effect of increasing the magnetic field strength.

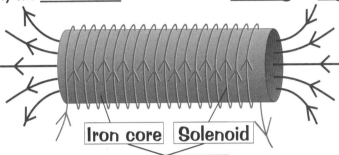

Iron core **Solenoid**

Electromagnet

1) The magnetic field around an electromagnet is just like the one round a bar magnet, only stronger.

2) This means that the ends of a solenoid act like the North Pole and South Pole of a bar magnet.

3) Pretty obviously, if the direction of the current is reversed, the N and S poles will swap ends.

4) If you imagine looking directly into one end of a solenoid, the direction of current flow tells you whether it's the N or S pole you're looking at, as shown by the two diagrams opposite. You need to remember those diagrams. They may show you a solenoid in the Exam and ask you which pole it is.

N-Pole **S-Pole**

The STRENGTH of an ELECTROMAGNET depends on THREE FACTORS:

1) The size of the *CURRENT*.
2) The number of *TURNS* the coil has.
3) What the *CORE* is made of.

Iron is Magnetically "Soft" — Ideal for Electromagnets

In magnetic terms, "soft" means it changes easily between being magnetised and demagnetised. Iron is "soft" which makes it perfect for electromagnets which need to be turned on and off.

Steel is Magnetically "Hard" — Ideal for Permanent Magnets

Magnetically "hard" means that the material retains its magnetism. This would be hopeless in an electromagnet, but is exactly what's required for permanent magnets.

To MAGNETISE a piece of steel, etc:

Put it in a solenoid with a steady DC supply. Turn off the current, pull it out, and there it is, a permanent magnet.

To DEMAGNETISE a piece of steel, etc:

Put it in a solenoid with an AC supply, and then pull it out with the AC current still going and there it is, demagnetised.

Magnetising - D.C. SUPPLY

Direct current

Demagnetising - A.C. SUPPLY

Alternating current

Electromagnets really irritate me — I just get solenoid with them...

This is all very basic information, and really quite memorable I'd have thought. Learn the headings and diagrams first, then cover the page and scribble them down. Then gradually fill in the other details. Keep looking back and checking. Try to learn all the points. Lovely innit.

Electromagnetic Devices

Electromagnets always have a soft iron core, which increases the strength of the magnet. The core has to be soft (magnetically soft, that is), so that when the current is turned off, the magnetism disappears with it. The four applications below depend on that happening.

Scrap yard Electromagnet

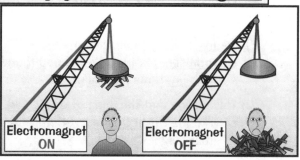

Electromagnet ON

Electromagnet OFF

1) The electromagnet consists of a big coil of wire, with many turns, and a soft iron core.
2) With the current on, this creates a very strong magnetic field, which attracts the scrap iron.

Circuit Breaker — or resettable fuse.

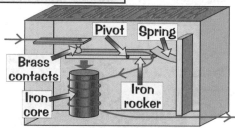

Pivot   Spring

Brass contacts

Iron core

Iron rocker

1) This is placed on the incoming live wire.
2) If the current gets too high, the magnetic field in the coil pulls the iron rocker which "trips" the switch and breaks the circuit.
3) It can be reset manually, but will always flick itself off if the current is too high.

Relay

eg: A relay is used in cars for safety when switching on the starter motor, because it draws a very big current.

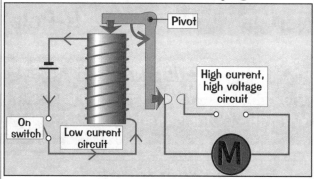

Pivot

High current, high voltage circuit

On switch

Low current circuit

M

1) A relay is a device which uses a low current circuit to switch a high current circuit on/off.
2) When the switch in the low current circuit is closed it turns the electromagnet on which attracts the iron rocker.
3) The rocker pivots and closes the contacts in the high current circuit.
4) When the low current switch is opened, the electromagnet stops pulling, the rocker returns, and the high current circuit is broken again.

Electric Bell

These are used in schools to stress everyone out.

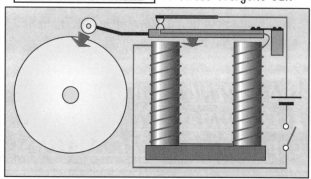

1) When the switch is closed, the electromagnets are turned on.
2) They pull the iron arm down which clangs the bell, but at the same time breaks the contact, which immediately turns off the electromagnets.
3) The arm then springs back, which closes the contact, and off we go again...
4) The whole sequence happens very quickly, maybe 10 times a second, so the bell sounds like a continuous "brrriiiinnngg" sound. Nice.

Only Iron, Steel and Nickel are Magnetic

Don't forget that all other common metals are not magnetic at all. So a magnet won't stick to aluminium ladders or copper kettles or brass trumpets or gold rings or silver spoons.

Learn about Magnets — it'll save you coming unstuck...

They nearly always have one of these in the Exam. Usually it's a circuit diagram of one of them and likely as not they'll ask you to explain exactly how it works. Make sure you learn all those tricky details for the three tricky ones. Cover, scribble, etc...

The Motor Effect

Anything <u>carrying a current</u> in a <u>magnetic field</u> will experience a <u>force</u>. There are <u>three important cases</u>:

A Current in a Magnetic Field Experiences a Force

The two tests below demonstrate the <u>force</u> on a <u>current-carrying wire</u> placed in a <u>magnetic field</u>.
The <u>force</u> gets <u>bigger</u> if either the <u>current</u> or the <u>magnetic field</u> is made bigger.

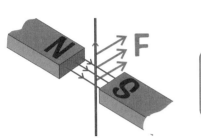

Horseshoe Magnet

Bar rolls along rails
when current is applied

1) Note that in <u>both cases</u> the <u>force</u> on the wire is at <u>90°</u> to both the <u>wire</u> and to the <u>magnetic field</u>.
2) You can always <u>predict</u> which way the <u>force</u> will act using <u>Fleming's LHR</u> as shown below.
3) To experience the <u>full force</u>, the <u>wire</u> has to be at <u>90°</u> to the <u>magnetic field</u>.
4) If the wire runs <u>along</u> the <u>magnetic field</u> it won't experience <u>any force at all</u>.
   At angles in between it'll feel <u>some</u> force.

The Simple Electric Motor

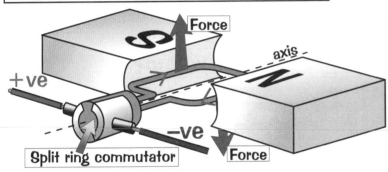

Force

axis

+ve

−ve

Force

Split ring commutator

4 Factors which Speed it up

1) More *CURRENT*
2) More *TURNS* on the coil
3) *STRONGER MAGNETIC FIELD*
4) A *SOFT IRON CORE* in the coil

1) The diagram shows the <u>forces</u> acting on the two <u>side arms</u> of the <u>coil</u>.

2) These forces are just the <u>usual forces</u> which act on <u>any current</u> in a <u>magnetic field</u>.

3) Because the coil is on a <u>spindle</u> and the forces act <u>one up</u> and <u>one down</u>, it <u>rotates</u>.

4) The <u>split ring commutator</u> is a clever way of "<u>swapping</u> the contacts <u>every half turn</u> to keep the motor rotating in the <u>same direction</u>". Learn that statement because they might ask you.

5) The direction of the motor can be <u>reversed</u> either by swapping the <u>polarity</u> of the <u>DC supply</u> or swapping the <u>magnetic poles</u> over.

Fleming's Left Hand Rule tells you Which way the Force Acts

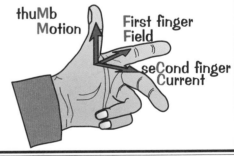

thuMb
Motion

First finger
Field

seCond finger
Current

1) They could test if you can do this, so <u>practise it</u>.

2) Using your <u>left hand</u>, point your <u>First finger</u> in the direction of the <u>Field</u> and your <u>seCond finger</u> in the direction of the <u>Current</u>.

3) Your <u>thuMb</u> will then point in the direction of the <u>force</u> *(Motion)*.

Loudspeakers Also Demonstrate the Motor Effect

1) <u>AC electrical signals</u> from the <u>amplifier</u> are fed to the <u>speaker coil</u> (shown red).
2) These make the coil move <u>back and forth</u> over the North pole of the <u>magnet</u>.
3) These movements make the <u>cardboard cone vibrate</u> and this creates <u>sounds</u>.

Fleming — how many broken wrists has he caused already...

Same old routine here. <u>Learn all the details</u>, diagrams and all, then <u>cover the page</u> and <u>scribble it all down</u> again <u>from memory</u>. You can scribble it as scruffy as you like — in pencil, biro, alphabetti-spagetti, who cares — all you're trying to do is make sure that you really do <u>know it</u>.

Electromagnetic Induction

Sounds terrifying. Well, sure it's quite mysterious, but it isn't that complicated:

> **ELECTROMAGNETIC INDUCTION:** The creation of a **_VOLTAGE_** (and maybe current)
> in a wire which is experiencing a **_CHANGE IN MAGNETIC FIELD_**.

For some reason they use the word "induction" rather than "creation", but it amounts to the same thing.

EM Induction — a) Flux cutting   b) Field Through a Coil

Electromagnetic induction is the induction of a voltage and/or current in a conductor.
There are two different situations where you get EM induction. You need to know about both of them:

    a) The conductor moves across a magnetic field and "cuts" through the lines of magnetic flux.
    b) The magnetic field through a closed coil changes, i.e. gets bigger or smaller or reverses.

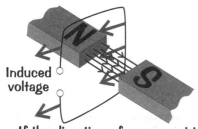

Induced voltage

If the direction of movement is reversed, then the voltage/current will be reversed too.

Four Factors Affect The Size of the Induced Voltage:

1) The **_STRENGTH_** of the **_MAGNET_**
2) The **_AREA_** of the **_COIL_**
3) The number of **_TURNS_** on the **_COIL_**
4) The **_SPEED_** of movement

These four factors can all be covered by one statement:

> The size of the **INDUCED VOLTAGE** is proportional to the **RATE OF CHANGE OF FLUX** through the circuit.

Ideally, you should be able to see how each one of the four factors means more flux is cut per second. Ideally.

Generators and Dynamos

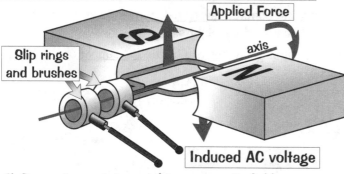

Applied Force

Slip rings and brushes

axis

Induced AC voltage

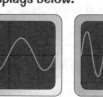
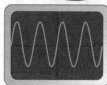

Dynamos are slightly different from generators because they rotate the magnet. This still causes the field through the coil to swap every half turn, so the output is just the same, as shown in the CRO displays below.

1) Generators rotate a coil in a magnetic field.

2) Their construction is pretty much like a motor.

3) The difference is the slip rings and brushes instead of a split ring commutator, so the contacts don't swap every half turn. The brushes are made of carbon.

4) This means they produce AC voltage, as shown by the CRO displays. Note that faster revs produce not only more peaks but higher overall voltage too.

"The Rate of Change of Flux" — pretty tricky isn't it...

"Electromagnetic Induction" gets my vote for "Definitely Most Trickiest Topic in GCSE Double Science". If it wasn't so important maybe you wouldn't have to bother learning it. The trouble is this is how all our electricity is generated. So it's pretty important. Learn and scribble...

Transformers

Transformers use Electromagnetic Induction. So they will only work on AC.

Transformers Change the Voltage — but only AC Voltages

Step-up transformers step the voltage up. They have more turns on the secondary coil.

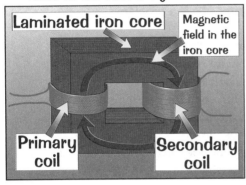

1) The laminated iron core is purely for transferring the magnetic flux from the primary coil to the secondary.

2) No electricity flows round the iron core, only magnetic flux.

3) The iron core is laminated with layers of insulation to reduce the eddy currents which heat it up, and therefore waste energy.

Step-down transformers step the voltage down. They have fewer turns on the secondary.

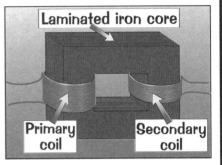

1) The primary coil produces magnetic flux (field) which stays within the iron core and this means it all passes through the secondary coil.

2) Because there is alternating current (AC) in the primary coil, this means that the flux in the iron core is constantly changing direction (100 times a second if it's at 50 Hz) — i.e. it is a changing flux.

3) This rapidly changing magnetic flux is then experienced by the secondary coil and this induces an alternating voltage in it — electromagnetic induction of a voltage in fact.

4) The relative number of turns on the two coils determines whether the voltage created in the secondary is greater or less than the voltage in the primary.

5) If you supplied DC to the primary, you'd get nothing out of the secondary at all. Sure, there'd still be flux in the iron core, but it wouldn't be constantly changing so there'd be no induction in the secondary because you need a changing flux to induce a voltage. Don't you!
So don't forget it — transformers only work with AC. They won't work with DC at all.

The Transformer Equation — use it Either Way Up

In words: The *RATIO OF TURNS* on the two coils equals the *RATIO OF THEIR VOLTAGES*.

$$\frac{\text{Primary Voltage}}{\text{Secondary Voltage}} = \frac{\text{Number of turns on Primary}}{\text{Number of turns on Secondary}}$$

$$\frac{V_P}{V_S} = \frac{N_P}{N_S}$$

or

$$\frac{V_S}{V_P} = \frac{N_S}{N_P}$$

Well, it's just another formula. You stick in the numbers you've got and work out the one that's left. It's really useful to remember you can write it either way up — this example's much trickier algebra-wise if you start with V_S on the bottom...

EXAMPLE: *A transformer has 40 turns on the primary and 800 on the secondary. If the input voltage is 1000 V find the output voltage.*

ANSWER: $V_S/V_P = N_S/N_P$ so $V_S/1000 = 800/40$ $V_S = 1000 \times (800/40) = $ 20,000 V

There's also "Power In = Power Out" which gives "$V_P I_P = V_S I_S$"

This formula is true because transformers are nearly 100% efficient. But don't panic, it's just another formula — you stick numbers in and work out the bit that's left, and that's all there is to it. End of story.

The ubiquitous Iron Core — where would we be without it...

Besides their iron core transformers have lots of other important details which also need to be learnt. You'll need to practise with those tricky equations too. They're unusual because they can't be put into formula triangles but other than that the method is the same. Just practise.

Revision Summary For Section One

Electricity and magnetism. What fun. This is definitely Physics at its most grisly. The big problem with Physics in general is that usually there's nothing to "see". You're told that there's a current flowing or a magnetic field lurking, but there's nothing you can actually see with your eyes. That's what makes it so difficult. To get to grips with Physics you have to get used to learning about things which you can't see. Try these questions and see how well you're doing.

1) What carries current in metals? What's "conventional current" and what's the problem?
2) Sketch CRO traces for DC and AC currents. Label the key features.
3) Sketch out the standard test circuit with all the details. Describe how it's used.
4) Sketch the four standard V-I graphs and explain their shapes. How do you get R from them?
5) Scribble down 18 circuit symbols that you know, with their names of course.
6) Write down two facts about: a) variable resistor   b) diode   c) LED   d) LDR   e) thermistor.
7) Sketch a typical series circuit and say why it is a series circuit, not a parallel one.
8) State five rules about the current, voltage and resistance in a series circuit.
9) Give examples of lights wired in series and wired in parallel and explain the main differences.
10) Sketch a typical parallel circuit, showing voltmeter and ammeter positions.
11) State five rules about the current, voltage and resistance in a parallel circuit.
12) Draw a circuit diagram of part of a car's electrics, and explain why they are in parallel.
13) What is static electricity? What is nearly always the cause of it building up?
14) Which particles move when static builds up, and which ones don't?
15) Explain how charging by induction works. Also explain what causes sparks to happen.
16) Give *two* examples each of static being: a) helpful b) a little joker c) a terrorist. Write all the details.
17) Look at the table on P. 8. Cover the last three columns and write down all the hidden details.
18) Explain how formula triangles work. What are the three rules for using any formula?
19) What are the two rules to remember about units? Give an example of each.
   a) Find the current when a resistance of 96 W is connected to a battery of 12V.
   b) Find the charge passed when a current of 2 A flows for 2 minutes.
   c) Find the power output of a heater which provides 77 kJ of heat energy in 4 mins.
   d) Find the resistance of a hairdrier which draws 10 Amps and gives out 1.4 kW.
20) What are the four types of energy that electricity can easily be converted into?
21) Sketch a circuit showing four devices converting energy. Describe all the energy changes.
22) Sketch a view of a circuit to explain the formula "E = QV". Which dull definitions go with it?
23) Go and look at the electricity meter where you live and explain what the number on it represents.
24) What's a kilowatt-hour? What are the two easy formulae for finding the cost of electricity?
25) Sketch a properly wired plug. Explain fully how fuses work.
26) Describe what earthing and double insulation are. Why are they useful?
27) Sketch a typical power station, and the national grid and explain why it's at 400 kV.
28) Sketch magnetic fields for: a) a bar magnet,   b) a solenoid, c) two magnets attracting,
   d) two magnets repelling, e) the Earth's magnetic field, f) a current-carrying wire.
29) What is an electromagnet made of? Explain how to decide on the polarity of the ends.
30) What is meant by magnetically hard and soft? How do you magnetise and demagnetise?
31) Sketch and give details of: a) Scrapyard magnet, b) Circuit breaker, c) Relay, d) Electric bell.
32) Sketch two demos of the motor effect. Sketch a motor and list the 4 factors which speed it up.
33) What do you use Fleming's Left Hand Rule for? Which direction do your fingers point in?
34) Give the definition of electromagnetic induction. Sketch three cases where it happens.
35) List the four factors which affect the size of the induced voltage.
36) Sketch a generator, labelling all the parts. Describe how it works and what all the bits do.
37) Write down how a dynamo works.
38) Sketch the two types of transformer, and highlight the main details. Explain how they work.
39) Write down the transformer equation. Do your own worked example — it's ace practice.

Numerical answers are on P.90.

Gravity, Weight and Moments

Gravity is the Force of Attraction Between All Masses

Gravity attracts all masses, but you only notice it when one of the masses is really really big, i.e. a planet. Anything near a planet or star is attracted to it very strongly. This has three important effects:

1) It makes all things accelerate towards the ground (all with the same acceleration, g, which » 10 m/s^2 on Earth).
2) It gives everything a weight.
3) It keeps planets, moons and satellites in their orbits. The orbit is a balance between the forward motion of the object and the force of gravity pulling it inwards.

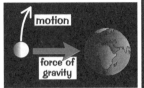

Weight and Mass are Not the Same

To understand this you must learn all these facts about mass and weight.

1) Mass is the amount of matter in an object. For any given object this will have the same value anywhere in the Universe.
2) Weight is caused by the pull of gravity. In most questions the weight of an object is just the force of gravity pulling it towards the centre of the Earth.
3) An object has the same mass whether it's on Earth or on the moon — but its weight will be different. A 1 kg mass will weigh less on the moon (1.6N) than it does on Earth (10N), simply because the force of gravity pulling on it is less.
4) Weight is a force measured in Newtons. It must be measured using a spring balance or Newton meter. Mass is not a force. It's measured in kilograms with a mass balance (never a spring balance).

The Very Important Formula relating Mass, Weight and Gravity

$$W = m \times g$$

(Weight = mass × g)

1) Remember, weight and mass are NOT the same. Mass is in kg, weight is in Newtons.
2) The letter "g" represents the strength of the gravity and its value is different for different planets. On Earth g = 10 N/kg. On the Moon, where the gravity is weaker, g is just 1.6 N/kg.
3) This formula is hideously easy to use:

EXAMPLE: *What is the weight, in Newtons, of a 5kg mass, both on Earth and on the Moon?*
ANSWER: *"W = m × g".   On Earth: W = 5 × 10 = 50N   (The weight of the 5kg mass is 50N)*
On the Moon: W = 5 × 1.6 = 8N   (The weight of the 5kg mass is 8N)
See what I mean. Hideously easy — as long as you've learnt what all the letters mean.

What's a Turning Force Called? — Just a Moment...

When a force acts on something which has a pivot, it creates a turning force called a "moment". Moments are calculated using this formula:

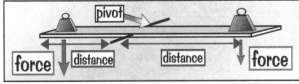

MOMENT = FORCE × PERPENDICULAR DISTANCE

Also, for the system to be in equilibrium, (i.e. all nicely balanced and not moving) then this must be true too:

TOTAL CLOCKWISE MOMENT = TOTAL ANTICLOCKWISE MOMENT

(You need to practise quite a few of these — ask your teacher for questions to try or get "Physics – The Formula Bits".)

Learn about gravity NOW — no point in "weighting" around...

Very often, the only way to "understand" something is to learn all the facts about it. That's certainly true here. "Understanding" the difference between mass and weight is no more than learning all those facts about them. When you've learnt all those facts, you'll understand it.

Force Diagrams

A <u>force</u> is simply a <u>push</u> or a <u>pull</u>. There are only <u>six different forces</u> for you to know about:

> 1) <u>GRAVITY</u> or <u>WEIGHT</u> always acting <u>straight downwards</u>.
> 2) <u>REACTION FORCE</u> from a <u>surface</u>, usually acting <u>straight upwards</u>.
> 3) <u>THRUST</u> or <u>PUSH</u> or <u>PULL</u> due to an engine or rocket <u>speeding something up</u>.
> 4) <u>DRAG</u> or <u>AIR RESISTANCE</u> or <u>FRICTION</u> which is <u>slowing the thing down</u>.
> 5) <u>LIFT</u> due to an <u>aeroplane wing</u>.
> 6) <u>TENSION</u> in a <u>rope</u> or <u>cable</u>.

And there are basically only <u>five different force diagrams</u> you can get:

1) Stationary Object — All Forces in Balance

1) The force of <u>GRAVITY</u> (or weight) is acting <u>downwards</u>.
2) This causes a <u>REACTION FORCE</u> from the surface <u>pushing</u> the object <u>back up</u>.
3) This is the <u>only way</u> it can be in <u>BALANCE</u>.
4) <u>Without</u> a reaction force, it would <u>accelerate downwards</u> due to the pull of gravity.
5) The two <u>HORIZONTAL</u> forces must be <u>equal and opposite</u> otherwise the object will <u>accelerate sideways</u>.

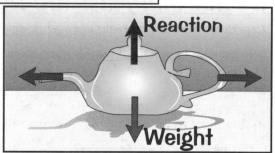

2) Steady Horizontal Velocity — All Forces in Balance!

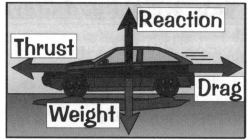

3) Steady Vertical Velocity — All Forces in Balance!

This skydiver is free-falling at 'terminal velocity' — see P.28.

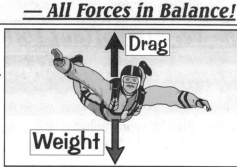

<u>Take note</u> — to move with a <u>steady speed</u> the forces must be in <u>balance</u>. If there is an <u>unbalanced force</u> then you get <u>acceleration</u>, not steady speed. That's <u>rrrreally important</u> so don't forget it.

4) Horizontal Acceleration — Unbalanced Forces

1) You only get <u>acceleration</u> with an overall <u>resultant</u> (unbalanced) <u>force</u>.
2) The <u>bigger</u> this <u>unbalanced force</u>, the <u>greater</u> the <u>acceleration</u>.

Note that the forces in the <u>other direction</u> are still <u>balanced</u>.

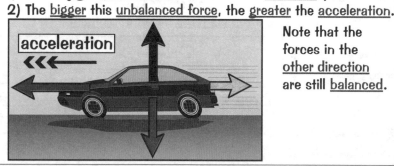

5) Vertical Acceleration — Unbalanced Forces

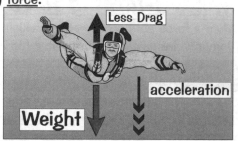

Just after dropping out of the plane, the skydiver accelerates — see P.28.

Revise Force Diagrams — but don't become unbalanced...

Make sure you learn those five different force diagrams. You'll almost certainly get one of them in your Exam. All you really need to remember is how the relative sizes of the arrows relate to the type of motion. It's pretty simple so long as you make the effort to <u>learn it</u>. So <u>scribble</u>...

Friction

1) Friction is Always There to Slow things Down

1) If an object has <u>no force</u> propelling it along, it will always <u>slow down and stop</u> because of <u>friction</u>.
2) To travel at a <u>steady speed</u>, things always need a <u>driving force</u> to counteract the friction.
3) Friction occurs in <u>three main ways</u>:

a) FRICTION BETWEEN SOLID SURFACES WHICH ARE GRIPPING

For example between <u>tyres and the road</u>. There's always a <u>limit</u> as to how far two surfaces can <u>grip</u> each other, and if you demand <u>more force of friction</u> than they can manage, then they start to <u>slide</u> past each other instead. i.e. if you try to brake <u>too hard</u>, you'll <u>skid</u>.

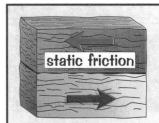

b) FRICTION BETWEEN SOLID SURFACES WHICH ARE SLIDING PAST EACH OTHER

For example between <u>brake pads and brake discs</u>. There's just as much force of <u>friction</u> here as between the tyres and the road. In fact in the end, if you brake hard enough, the friction here becomes <u>greater</u> than at the tyres, and then the wheel <u>skids</u>.

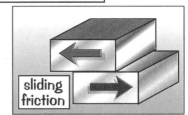

c) RESISTANCE OR "DRAG" FROM FLUIDS (AIR OR LIQUID)

The most important factor <u>by far</u> in <u>reducing drag in fluids</u> is keeping the shape of the object <u>streamlined</u>, like fish bodies or boat hulls or bird wings/bodies. The <u>opposite extreme</u> is a <u>parachute</u> which is about as <u>high drag</u> as you can get — which is, of course, <u>the whole idea</u>.

2) Friction Always Increases as the Speed Increases

A car has <u>much more friction</u> to <u>work against</u> when travelling at <u>60mph</u> compared to <u>30mph</u>. So at 60mph the engine has to work <u>much harder</u> just to maintain a <u>steady speed</u>.
It therefore uses <u>more petrol</u> than it would going just as far at 30mph.

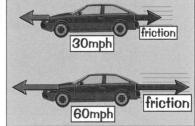

3) But We Also Need Friction to Move and to Stop!

It's easy to think of friction as generally a <u>nuisance</u> because we always seem to be working <u>against it</u>, but don't forget that <u>without it</u> we wouldn't be able to <u>walk</u> or <u>run</u> or <u>race off the line at the traffic lights</u> or <u>screech round corners</u> or go <u>sky-diving</u> or do just about anything exciting or interesting. It also holds <u>nuts and bolts</u> together. Life <u>without</u> friction — that <u>would</u> be a drag.

4) Friction Causes Wear and Heating

1) Friction always acts <u>between surfaces</u> that are <u>sliding over</u> each other. <u>Machinery</u> has lots of surfaces doing that.
2) Friction always produces <u>heat</u> and <u>wearing</u> of the surfaces.
3) <u>LUBRICANTS</u> are used to keep the friction as <u>low</u> as possible.
4) These make the machinery run more <u>freely</u> so it needs <u>less power</u>, and it also <u>reduces wear</u>.
5) The <u>heating effect</u> of friction can be <u>enormous</u>. For example the <u>brakes</u> on <u>grand prix racing cars</u> can often <u>glow red hot</u>. Another example is if an engine runs <u>without oil</u> it will quickly <u>seize up</u> as the moving parts get <u>red hot</u> through friction and eventually <u>weld</u> themselves together.

Learn about friction — just don't let it wear you down...

I would never have thought there was so much to say about friction. Nevertheless, there it all is, all mentioned in the syllabuses, and all very likely to come up in your Exam. Ignore it at your peril. <u>Learn</u> the seven main headings, then the stuff, then <u>cover the page</u> and away you go.

The Three Laws of Motion

Around about the time of the Great Plague in the 1660s, a chap called Isaac Newton worked out The Three Laws of Motion. At first they might seem kind of obscure or irrelevant, but to be perfectly blunt, if you can't understand these three simple laws then you'll never fully understand forces and motion:

First Law — Balanced Forces mean No Change in Velocity

So long as the forces on an object are all *BALANCED*, then it'll just *STAY STILL*, or else if it's already moving it'll just carry on at the *SAME VELOCITY* — so long as the forces are all *BALANCED*.

1) When a train or car or bus or anything else is moving at a constant velocity then the forces on it must all be balanced.

2) Never allow yourself to entertain the ridiculous idea that things need a constant overall force to keep them moving — NO NO NO NO NO NO!

3) To keep going at a steady speed, there must be zero resultant force — and don't you forget it.

Second Law — A Resultant Force means Acceleration

If there is an *UNBALANCED FORCE*, then the object will *ACCELERATE* in that direction. The size of the acceleration is decided by the formula: F = ma.

1) An unbalanced force will always produce acceleration (or deceleration).

2) This "acceleration" can take five different forms: Starting, stopping, speeding up, slowing down and changing direction.

3) On a force diagram, the arrows will be unequal:

Don't ever say: "If something's moving there must be an overall resultant force acting on it". Not so. If there's an overall force it will always accelerate. You get steady speed from balanced forces. I wonder how many times I need to say that same thing before you remember it?

The Overall Unbalanced Force is often called The Resultant Force

Any resultant force will produce acceleration and this is the formula for it:

$$ F = ma \quad \text{or} \quad a = F/m $$

m = mass, a = acceleration, F is always the resultant force
(See P. 9 on using formulas)

Three Points Which Should Be Obvious:

1) The bigger the force, the greater the acceleration or deceleration.

2) The bigger the mass, the smaller the acceleration.

3) To get a big mass to accelerate as fast as a small mass, it needs a bigger force. Just think about pushing heavy trolleys and it should all seem fairly obvious, I would hope.

The Three Laws of Motion

Calculations using F = ma — Two Examples

Q1) *What force is needed to accelerate a mass of 12kg at 5m/s² ?*

Ans. The question is asking for <u>force</u>

— so you need a formula with "<u>F = something-or-other</u>".

Since they also give you values for <u>mass</u> and <u>acceleration</u>, the
formula "<u>F = ma</u>" really should be a <u>pretty obvious choice</u>, surely.

So just <u>stick in the numbers</u> they give you where the letters are:

<u>m = 12</u>, <u>a = 5</u>, so "<u>F = ma</u>" gives F = 12 × 5 = <u>60N</u>   (It's <u>Newtons</u> because force always is)

(Notice that you don't really need to <u>fully understand</u> what's going on — you just need to know <u>how to use formulae</u>.)

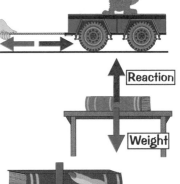

Q2) *The same force acts on another mass and it accelerates at 6m/s². What is its mass?*

ANS. The question mentions <u>force</u>, <u>mass</u> and <u>acceleration</u>, so the formula to use is still "F = ma".

But this time you have to find <u>m</u>, which means using the <u>formula triangle</u>.

<u>Cover up m</u> to get: "<u>m = F/a</u>" (m = F ÷ a)

Since <u>F = 60N</u> and <u>a = 6m/s²</u> we stick these in to get: m = 60/6 = <u>10kg</u>.   Easy innit?

The Third Law — Reaction Forces

> If object A *EXERTS A FORCE* on object B then object B
> exerts *THE EXACT OPPOSITE FORCE* on object A

1) That means if you <u>push against a wall</u>, the wall will <u>push back</u> against
   you, <u>just as hard</u>.

2) And as soon as you <u>stop</u> pushing, <u>so does the wall</u>. Kinda clever really.

3) If you think about it, there must be an <u>opposing force</u> when you lean
   against a wall — otherwise you (and the wall) would <u>fall over</u>.

4) If you <u>pull a cart</u>, whatever force <u>you exert</u> on the rope, the rope exerts
   the <u>exact opposite</u> pull on <u>you</u>.

5) If you put a book on a table, the <u>weight</u> of the book acts <u>downwards</u> on
   the table, — and the table exerts an <u>equal and opposite</u> force <u>upwards</u>
   on the book.

6) If you support a book on your <u>hand</u>, the book exerts its <u>weight</u>
   downwards on you, and you provide an <u>upwards</u> force on the book
   and it all stays <u>nicely in balance</u>.

In <u>Exam questions</u> they may well <u>test this</u> by getting you to fill in some
<u>extra arrow</u> to represent the <u>reaction force</u>. Learn this <u>very important fact</u>:

> Whenever an object is on a horizontal <u>SURFACE</u>,
> there'll always be a *REACTION FORCE* pushing
> <u>UPWARDS</u>, supporting the object.
> The total *REACTION FORCE* will be *EQUAL*
> *AND OPPOSITE* to the weight.

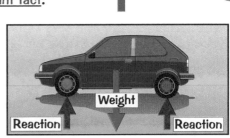

Hey, did you know — an unbalanced force upsets Yoda...

Good old Isaac. Those three laws of motion are pretty inspirational don't you think? No? Oh.
Well you could do with learning them anyway, because in this topic there are hardly any nice
easy facts that'll help — in the end there's <u>no substitute</u> for fully understanding <u>The Three Laws</u>.

Speed, Velocity and Acceleration

Speed and Velocity are Both just: HOW FAST YOU'RE GOING

Speed and velocity are both measured in m/s (or km/h or mph). They both simply say how fast you're going, but there's a subtle difference between them which you need to know:

SPEED is just how fast you're going (e.g. 30mph or 20m/s) with no regard to the direction.
VELOCITY however must also have the DIRECTION specified, e.g. 30mph *north* or 20m/s, 060°

Seems kinda fussy I know, but they expect you to remember that distinction, so there you go.

Speed, Distance and Time — the Formula:

$$\text{Speed} = \frac{\text{Distance}}{\text{Time}}$$

You really ought to get pretty slick with this very easy formula.
As usual the formula triangle version makes it all a bit of a breeze.
You just need to try and think up some interesting word for remembering the order of the letters in the triangle, s^{d}t.   Errm... sedit, perhaps... well, I'm sure you can think up something better...

EXAMPLE: A cat skulks 20m in 35s. Find   a) its speed   b) how long it takes to skulk 75m.
ANSWER: *Using the formula triangle:*   a) s = d/t = 20/35 = 0.57m/s
b) t = d/s = 75/0.57 = 131s = 2mins 11sec

A lot of the time we tend to use the words "speed" and "velocity" interchangeably.
For example to calculate velocity you'd just use the above formula for speed.

Acceleration is How Quickly You're Speeding Up

Acceleration is definitely not the same as velocity or speed.
   Every time you read or write the word acceleration, remind yourself: "acceleration is completely different from velocity. Acceleration is how quickly the velocity is changing."
Velocity is a simple idea. Acceleration is altogether more subtle, which is why it's confusing.

Acceleration — The Formula:

$$\text{Acceleration} = \frac{\text{Change in Velocity}}{\text{Time Taken}}$$

Well, it's just another formula. Just like all the others. Three things in a formula triangle.
Mind you, there are two tricky things with this one. First there's the "ΔV", which means working out the "change in velocity", as shown in the example below, rather than just putting a simple value for speed or velocity in.   Secondly there's the units of acceleration which are m/s^2.
Not m/s, which is velocity, but m/s^2. Got it? No?   Let's try once more: Not m/s, but m/s^2.

EXAMPLE: A skulking cat accelerates from 2m/s to 6m/s in 5.6s. Find its acceleration.
ANSWER: *Using the formula triangle:*   a = ΔV/t = (6 - 2) / 5.6 = 4 ÷ 5.6 = 0.71 m/s^2
All pretty basic stuff I'd say.

Velocity and Acceleration — learn the difference...

It's true — some people don't realise that velocity and acceleration are totally different things.
Hard to believe I know — all part of the great mystery and tragedy of life I suppose.
Anyway. Learn the definitions and the formulae, cover the page and scribble it all down again.

Distance-Time and Velocity-Time Graphs

Make sure you learn all these details real good. Make sure you can <u>distinguish</u> between the two, too.

Distance-Time Graphs

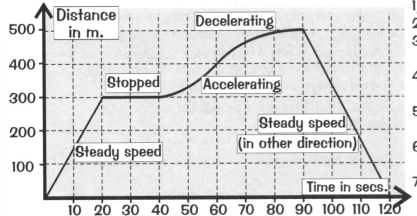

Very Important Notes:

1) <u>GRADIENT = SPEED</u>.
2) <u>Flat sections</u> are where it's <u>stopped</u>.
3) The <u>steeper</u> the graph, the <u>faster</u> it's going.
4) <u>Downhill</u> sections mean it's <u>coming back</u> toward its starting point.
5) <u>Curves</u> represent <u>acceleration</u> or deceleration.
6) A <u>steepening curve</u> means it's <u>speeding up</u> (increasing gradient).
7) A <u>levelling off curve</u> means it's <u>slowing down</u> (decreasing gradient).

Calculating Speed from a Distance-Time Graph — it's just the Gradient

For example the <u>speed</u> of the <u>return section</u> of the graph is:

<u>Speed</u> = <u>gradient</u> = $\dfrac{\text{vertical}}{\text{horizontal}}$ = $\dfrac{500}{30}$ = <u>16.7 m/s</u>

Don't forget that you have to use the <u>scales of the axes</u> to work out the gradient. <u>Don't measure in cm</u>.

Velocity-Time Graphs

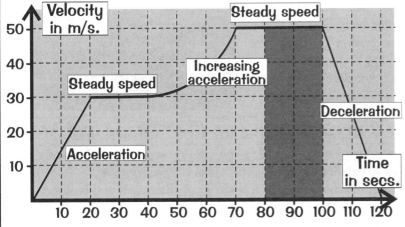

Very Important Notes:

1) <u>GRADIENT = ACCELERATION</u>.
2) <u>Flat sections</u> represent <u>steady speed</u>.
3) The <u>steeper</u> the graph, the <u>greater</u> the <u>acceleration</u> or deceleration.
4) <u>Uphill</u> sections (/) are <u>acceleration</u>.
5) <u>Downhill</u> sections (\\) — <u>deceleration</u>.
6) The <u>area</u> under any section of the graph (or all of it) is equal to the <u>distance travelled</u> in that <u>time interval</u>.
7) A <u>curve</u> means <u>changing acceleration</u>.

Calculating Acceleration, Speed and Distance from a Velocity-time Graph

1) The <u>acceleration</u> represented by the <u>first section</u> of the graph is:

    <u>Acceleration</u> = <u>gradient</u> = $\dfrac{\text{vertical}}{\text{horizontal}}$ = $\dfrac{30}{20}$ = <u>1.5 m/s²</u>

2) The <u>speed</u> at any point is simply found by <u>reading the value</u> off the <u>speed axis</u>.

3) The <u>distance travelled</u> in any time interval is equal to the <u>area</u>. For example, the distance travelled between t = 80 and t = 100 is equal to the <u>shaded area</u> which is equal to <u>1000m</u>.

Understanding speed and stuff — it can be an uphill struggle...

The tricky thing about these two kinds of graph is that they can look pretty much the same but represent totally different kinds of motion. If you want to be able to do them (in the Exam) then there's no substitute for simply <u>learning all the numbered points</u> for both types. Enjoy.

Resultant Force and Terminal Velocity

Resultant Force is Real Important — Especially for "F = ma"

The notion of resultant force is a real important one for you to get your head round.

It's not especially tricky, it's just that it seems to get kind of ignored.

In most real situations there are at least two forces acting on an object along any direction.

The overall effect of these forces will decide the motion of the object — whether it will accelerate, decelerate or stay at a steady speed. The "overall effect" is found by just adding or subtracting the forces which point along the same direction. The overall force you get is called the resultant force.

And when you use the formula "F = ma", F must always be the resultant force.

EXAMPLE: A car of mass of 1750kg has an engine which provides a driving force of 5,200N.
At 70mph the drag force acting on the car is 5,150N.
Find its acceleration a) when first setting off from rest b) at 70mph.

ANSWER: 1) First draw a force diagram for both cases (no need to show the vertical forces):

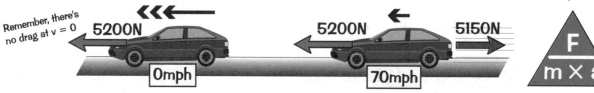

Remember, there's no drag at v = 0
5200N — 0mph
5200N — 5150N — 70mph

2) Work out the resultant force in each case, and apply "F = ma" using the formula triangle:

Resultant force = 5,200N
a = F/m = 5,200 ÷ 1750 = 3.0 m/s^2

Resultant force = 5,200 − 5,150 = 50N
a = F/m = 50 ÷ 1750 = 0.03 m/s^2

Cars and Free-Fallers all Reach a Terminal Velocity

When cars and free-falling objects first set off they have much more force accelerating them than resistance slowing them down. As the speed increases the resistance builds up. This gradually reduces the acceleration until eventually the resistance force is equal to the accelerating force and then it won't be able to accelerate any more. It will have reached its maximum speed or terminal velocity.

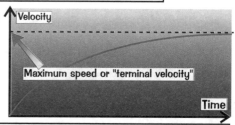

Velocity

Maximum speed or "terminal velocity"

Time

The Terminal Velocity of Falling Objects depends on their Shape and Area

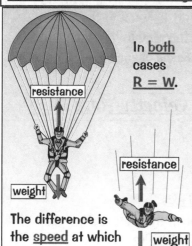

In both cases R = W.

resistance

weight

resistance

weight

The difference is the speed at which that happens.

The accelerating force acting on all falling objects is gravity and it would make them all fall at the same rate, if it wasn't for air resistance.

To prove this, on the moon, where there's no air, hamsters and feathers dropped simultaneously will hit the ground together.

However, on Earth, air resistance causes things to fall at different speeds, and the terminal velocity of any object is determined by its drag in comparison to the weight of it. The drag depends on its shape and area.

The most important example is the human skydiver. Without his parachute open he has quite a small area and a force of "W=mg" pulling him down. He reaches a terminal velocity of about 120mph.

But with the parachute open, there's much more air resistance (at any given speed) and still only the same force "W=mg" pulling him down.

This means his terminal velocity comes right down to about 15mph, which is a safe speed to hit the ground at.

Learning about air resistance — it can be a real drag...

It looks like mini-essay time to me. There's a lot of details swirling around here, so definitely the best way of checking how much you know is to scribble down a mini-essay for each of the three sections. Then check back and see what you missed. Then try again. And keep trying.

Stopping Distances For Cars

They're pretty keen on this for Exam questions, so make sure you <u>learn it properly</u>.

The Many Factors Which Affect Your Total Stopping Distance

The distance it takes to stop a car is divided into the <u>thinking distance</u> and the <u>braking distance</u>.

1) Thinking Distance

"<u>The distance the car travels in the split-second between a hazard appearing and the driver applying the brakes</u>." It's affected by <u>three main factors</u>:

a) How FAST you're going — obviously. Whatever your reaction time, the <u>faster</u> you're going, the <u>further</u> you'll go.

b) How DOPEY you are — This is affected by <u>tiredness</u>, <u>drugs</u>, <u>alcohol</u>, <u>old-age</u>, and a <u>careless</u> blasé attitude.

c) How BAD the VISIBILITY is — lashing rain and oncoming lights, etc. make <u>hazards</u> harder to spot.

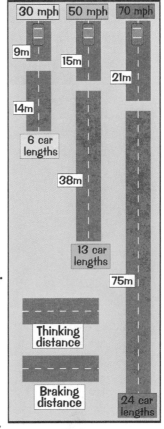

The figures below for typical stopping distances are from the Highway code. It's frightening to see just how far it takes to stop when you're going at 70mph.

2) Braking Distance

"<u>The distance the car travels during its deceleration whilst the brakes are being applied</u>." It's affected by <u>four main factors</u>:

a) How FAST you're going — obviously. The <u>faster</u> you're going the <u>further</u> it takes to stop (see below).

b) How HEAVILY LOADED the vehicle is — with the <u>same</u> brakes, a heavily-laden vehicle takes <u>longer to stop</u>. A car won't stop as quick when it's full of people and luggage and towing a caravan.

c) How good your BRAKES are — all brakes must be <u>checked and maintained regularly</u>. Worn or faulty brakes will let you down <u>catastrophically</u> just when you need them the <u>most</u>, i.e. in an <u>emergency</u>.

d) How good the GRIP is — this depends on <u>three things</u>: 1) <u>road surface</u>, 2) <u>weather</u> conditions, 3) <u>tyres</u>.

Leaves and diesel spills and muck on t'road are <u>serious hazards</u> because they're <u>unexpected</u>. <u>Wet</u> or <u>icy roads</u> are always <u>much more slippy</u> than dry roads, but often you only discover this when you try to <u>brake</u> hard. Tyres should have a minimum <u>tread depth</u> of <u>1.6mm</u>. This is essential for <u>getting rid of the water</u> in wet conditions. <u>Without tread</u>, a tyre will simply <u>ride</u> on a <u>layer of water</u> and skid <u>very easily</u>. This is called "<u>aquaplaning</u>" and isn't nearly as cool as it sounds.

Stopping Distances Increase Alarmingly with Extra Speed

— Mainly Because of the V² bit in KE=½mv²

To stop a car, the <u>kinetic energy</u>, ½mv², has to be <u>converted to heat energy</u> at the <u>brakes and tyres</u>:

Kinetic Energy Transferred = Work Done by Brakes
$$\tfrac{1}{2}mv^2 = f \times d$$

(See P. 66 on Energy and Work)

v = <u>speed</u> of car   f = maximum <u>braking force</u>   d = <u>braking distance</u>

<u>Learn this real good</u>: if you <u>double the speed</u>, you double the value of v, but the v² means that the <u>KE</u> is then increased by a factor of <u>four</u>. However, "f" is always the <u>maximum possible</u> braking force which <u>can't</u> be increased, so <u>d</u> must also increase by a factor of <u>four</u> to make the equation <u>balance</u>. i.e. if you go <u>twice as fast</u>, the <u>braking distance</u> "d" must increase by a <u>factor of four</u> to dissipate the <u>extra KE</u>.

Muck on t'road, eh — by gum, it's grim up North...

They mention this specifically in the syllabus and are very likely to test you on it since it involves safety. Learn all the details and write yourself a <u>mini-essay</u> to see how much you <u>really know</u>.

Hooke's Law

Hooke's Law — Extension is Proportional to Load

Hooke's Law is <u>seriously easy</u>. It just says:

> If you **_STRETCH_** something with a **_STEADILY INCREASING
> FORCE_**, then the **_LENGTH_** will **_INCREASE STEADILY_** too.

The important thing to measure in a Hooke's Law experiment
is not so much the total length as the <u>extension</u>,

> **_EXTENSION_** is the **_INCREASE IN LENGTH_**
> compared to the original length
> with <u>no force applied</u>.

For most materials, you'll find that the
EXTENSION IS PROPORTIONAL TO THE LOAD,
which just means if you <u>double</u> the load, the
<u>extension is double too</u>.

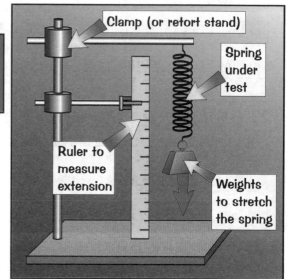

Clamp (or retort stand)

Spring under test

Ruler to measure extension

Weights to stretch the spring

You should **LEARN** that this always gives a <u>straight line</u>
graph through the <u>origin</u>, as shown here. This is the
graph you get for the <u>two important cases</u>: a <u>metal wire</u>
and a <u>spring</u>.

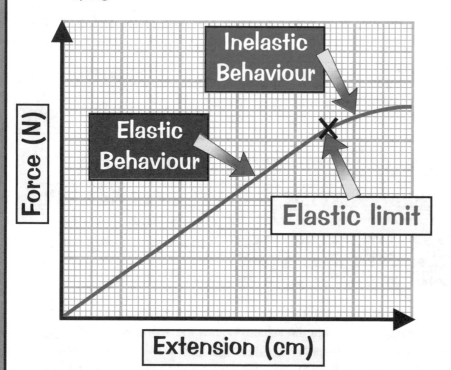

Inelastic Behaviour

Elastic Behaviour

Elastic limit

Force (N)

Extension (cm)

Notice that for both the <u>wire</u> and
the <u>spring</u>, there's an <u>elastic limit</u>.
For extensions <u>less</u> than this, the
wire or spring <u>returns to its
original shape</u>, but if stretched
<u>beyond</u> the elastic limit, it
behaves <u>inelastically</u>, which means
it <u>doesn't</u> follow Hooke's Law and
that it also <u>won't return</u> to its
original shape.

Hooke's Law — it can stretch you to the limit...

Hooke's Law is pretty standard stuff, so make sure you know all the little details. You've got to
be able to draw the graph, label it right and <u>explain</u> the ideas behind the straight bit and the
curved bit. Find out what you know: <u>cover, scribble, check</u>, etc.

Boyle's Law: $P_1V_1 = P_2V_2$

<u>Boyle's law</u> sounds a lot more confusing than it actually is. This is the fancy definition:

When the ***PRESSURE IS INCREASED*** on a <u>fixed mass of gas</u> kept at <u>constant temperature</u>, the ***VOLUME WILL DECREASE***. The changes in pressure and volume are in ***INVERSE PROPORTION***.

If you ask me it's a pretty <u>obvious</u> way for a gas to behave. In simple language it's just this:

If you squash a gas into a smaller space, the pressure goes up in proportion to how much you squash it. E.g. if you squash it to half the amount of space, it'll end up at twice the pressure it was before (so long as you don't let it get hotter or colder, or let any escape). Simple, innit?

It can work <u>both ways</u> too. If you <u>increase the pressure</u>, the <u>volume must decrease</u>.
If you <u>increase the volume</u>, the <u>pressure must decrease</u>. That's all pretty obvious though isn't it?

Gas Syringe Experiments Are Good For Showing Boyle's Law

1) A <u>gas syringe</u> makes a pretty good <u>airtight seal</u> and is great for demonstrating <u>Boyle's Law</u>.

2) You put <u>weights on the top</u> to give a <u>definite</u> known force pushing down on the piston.

3) If you <u>double the weight</u>, you also <u>double the force</u> which <u>doubles the pressure</u>.

4) You can then measure the <u>volume change</u> using the <u>scale</u> on the side of the syringe. Easy peasy.

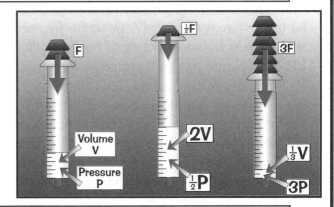

Using the Formula "PV = Constant" or "$P_1V_1 = P_2V_2$"

Well what can I say, it's another formula. Not quite one you can put in a triangle, but still the same old idea: <u>stick in the numbers</u> they give you, and <u>work out the value</u> for the remaining letter. Please try and get it into your head that you don't need to <u>fully understand</u> the Physics, you just need a bit of "common sense" about <u>formulae</u>. Understanding always helps of course, but you can still get the right answer without it! Really, you've just got to identify the values for each letter — the rest is <u>very routine</u>.
<u>EXAMPLE</u>: *A gas is compressed from a volume of 300cm³ at a pressure of 2.5 atmospheres down to a volume of 175cm³. Find the new pressure, in atmospheres.*
<u>ANSWER</u>: "$P_1V_1 = P_2V_2$" gives: $2.5 \times 300 = P_2 \times 175$, so $P_2 = (2.5 \times 300) \div 175 = 4.3$ atm.
NB For <u>this formula</u>, always keep the units <u>the same</u> as they give them (in this case, pressure in <u>atmospheres</u>)

Kinetic Theory Explains it all Very Nicely

1) The <u>pressure</u> which a gas <u>exerts</u> on the <u>container</u> is caused by the particles whizzing about and <u>bashing into the walls</u> of the container. It depends on <u>two things</u>: how <u>fast</u> they're going and <u>how often</u> they hit the walls.

2) <u>How often</u> they hit the walls depends on how <u>squashed up</u> they are. When the <u>volume is reduced</u>, the particles become <u>more squashed up</u> and so they hit the walls <u>more often</u>, and hence the <u>pressure increases</u>. The <u>speed</u> of the particles <u>won't change</u> so long as the <u>temperature</u> doesn't change.

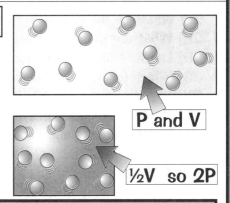

P and V

½V so 2P

Less space, more collisions, more pressure — just like London...

This is another topic that can seem a lot more confusing than it really is. The basic principle of Boyle's Law is simple enough, and so is the Gas Syringe demo. The formula might look bad but really there's nothing to it. In the end it's just stuff that needs <u>learning</u>, that's all. <u>Scribble</u>.

Revision Summary for Section Two

More jolly questions which I know you're going to really enjoy. There are lots of bits and bobs on forces and motion which you definitely need to know. Some bits are certainly quite tricky to understand, but there's also loads of straightforward stuff which just needs to be learned, ready for instant regurgitation in the Exam. You have to practise these questions over and over and over again, until you can answer them all really easily — phew, such jolly fun.

Burgundy questions are for Edexcel bods <u>only</u>.

1) What is gravity? List the three main effects that gravity produces.
2) Explain the difference between mass and weight. What units are they measured in?
3) What's the formula for weight? Illustrate it with a worked example of your own.
4) List the six different kinds of force. Sketch diagrams to illustrate them all.
5) Sketch each of the five standard force diagrams, showing the forces and the type of motion.
6) List the three types of friction with a sketch to illustrate each one.
7) Describe how friction is affected by speed. What 2 effects does friction have on machinery?
8) Is friction at all useful? Describe five problems we would have if there was no friction.
9) Write down the First Law of Motion. Illustrate with a diagram.
10) If an object has zero resultant force on it, can it be moving? Can it be accelerating?
11) Write down the Second Law of Motion. Illustrate with a diagram. What's the formula for it?
12) A force of 30N pushes on a trolley of mass 4kg. What will be its acceleration?
13) What's the mass of a cat which accelerates at 9.8 m/s² when acted on by a force of 56N?
14) Write down the Third Law of Motion. Illustrate it with four diagrams.
15) Explain what *reaction force* is and where it pops up. Is it important to know about it?
16) What's the difference between speed and velocity? Give an example of each.
17) Write down the formula for working out speed. Find the speed of a partly chewed mouse which hobbles 3.2m in 35s. Find how far he would get in 25 minutes.
18) What's acceleration? Is it the same thing as speed or velocity? What are the units of it?
19) Write down the formula for acceleration.
    What's the acceleration of a soggy pea, flicked from rest to a speed of 14 m/s in 0.4s?
20) Sketch a typical distance-time graph and point out all the important parts of it.
21) Sketch a typical velocity-time graph and point out all the important parts of it.
22) Write down seven important points relating to each of these graphs.
23) Explain how to calculate velocity from a distance-time graph.
24) Explain how to find speed, distance and acceleration from a velocity-time graph.
25) Explain what "resultant force" is. Illustrate with a diagram. When do you most need it?
26) What is "terminal velocity"? Is it the same thing as maximum speed?
27) What are the two main factors affecting the terminal velocity of a falling object?
28) What are the two different parts of the overall stopping distance of a car?
29) List the three or four factors which affect each of the two parts of stopping distance.
30) Which formula explains why the stopping distance increases so much? Explain why it does.
31) What is Hooke's Law? Sketch the usual apparatus. Explain what you must measure.
32) Sketch the Hooke's Law graph for a spring and explain its shape.
    Explain "elastic" and "inelastic".
33) What is Boyle's Law? Sketch an experiment which demonstrates it. What's the formula?
34) A fixed amount of gas at 5,000 Pa is compressed down to 60cm³, and in the process its pressure rises to 260,000 Pa. What was the volume before it got compressed?
35) What does Kinetic Theory say affects the pressure on the walls of a container of gas?
36) What happens to particles in a gas if you reduce the volume?
    What happens to the pressure?

Numerical answers are on P.90.

Waves — Basic Principles

Waves are different from anything else. They have various features which only waves have:

Amplitude, Wavelength, Frequency and Period

Too many people get these wrong. Take careful note:

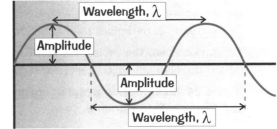

1) The AMPLITUDE goes from the middle line to the peak, NOT from a trough to a peak.

2) The WAVELENGTH covers a full cycle of the wave, e.g. from peak to peak, not just from *"two bits that are sort of separated a bit"*.

3) FREQUENCY is how many complete waves there are per second (passing a certain point). Frequency is measured in Hertz. 1 Hz is 1 complete wave per second.

4) The PERIOD is the time taken for one complete wave.   The formula is $T = 1/f$

Transverse Waves have Sideways Vibrations

Most waves are transverse:

1) Light and all other EM waves.

2) Ripples on water.

3) Waves on strings.

4) A slinky spring wiggled up and down.

In **TRANSVERSE** waves the vibrations are at 90^0 to the **DIRECTION OF TRAVEL** of the wave.

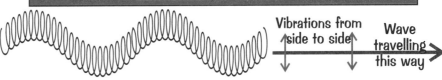

Vibrations from side to side

Wave travelling this way

Longitudinal Waves have Vibrations along the Same Line

The ONLY longitudinal waves are:

1) Sound waves.

2) Shock waves e.g. seismic P-waves (See P. 48).

3) A slinky spring when plucked.

In **LONGITUDINAL** waves the vibrations are along the **SAME DIRECTION** as the wave is travelling.

One wavelength   Rarefactions

Compressions

Vibrations in same direction

as wave is travelling

4) Don't get confused by CRO displays which show a transverse wave when displaying sounds. The real sound wave is longitudinal — the display shows a transverse wave just so you can see what's going on.

All Waves Carry Energy — Without Transferring Matter

1) Light, infra red, and microwaves all make things warm up. X-rays and gamma rays can cause ionisation and damage to cells, which also shows that they carry energy.

2) Loud sounds make things vibrate or move. Even the quietest sound moves your ear drum.

3) Waves on the sea can toss big boats around and can generate electricity.

4) Waves also transfer information, as well as energy, e.g. TV, radio, speech, fibre optics, etc.

Waves can be REFLECTED and REFRACTED and DIFFRACTED

See P.39 – 41 and P.44 for these topics.

They might test whether or not you realise these are properties of waves, so learn them. The three words are confusingly similar but you must learn the differences between them.

Learn about waves — just get into the vibes, man...

This is all very basic stuff on waves. Four sections with four points in each. Learn the headings, then the details. Then cover the page and see what you can scribble down. Then try again and again until you can remember the whole lot. It's all just easy marks to be won... or lost.

Sound Waves

1) Sound Travels at Various Speeds in Different Substances

1) Sound Waves are caused by vibrating objects.

2) Sound waves are longitudinal waves, which travel at fixed speeds in particular media, as shown in the table.

3) As you can see, the denser the medium, the faster sound travels through it, generally speaking anyway.

4) Sound generally travels faster in solids than in liquids, and faster in liquids than in gases.

Substance	Density	Speed of Sound
Iron	7.9 g/cm³	5000 m/s
Rubber	0.9 g/cm³	1600 m/s
Water	1.0 g/cm³	1400 m/s
Cork	0.3 g/cm³	500 m/s
Air	0.001 g/cm³	330 m/s

2) Sound Doesn't Travel In A Vacuum

1) Sound waves can be reflected, refracted and diffracted.

2) But one thing they can't do is travel through a vacuum.

3) This is nicely demonstrated by the jolly old bell jar experiment.

4) As the air is sucked out by the vacuum pump, the sound gets quieter and quieter.

5) The bell has to be mounted on something like foam to stop the sound from it travelling through the solid surface and making the bench vibrate, because you'd hear that instead.

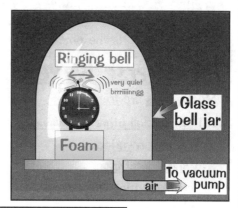

3) Your Hearing can be Damaged by Excessive Noise

1) The normal range of human hearing is 20 Hz to 20,000 Hz, but the upper limit decreases with age. Sounds with frequencies above 20,000 Hz just can't be heard. Not by humans anyway.

2) Dogs however can hear up to about 40,000 Hz so dog whistles whistle between 20kHz and 40 kHz so we can't hear them but the dogs can.

3) Too much loud noise will damage your hearing. The higher end of the frequency range is affected more. Personal stereos and loud machinery are the main culprits for wrecking people's hearing.

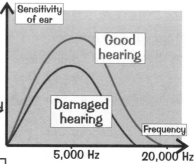

4) Noise Pollution — an Increasing Menace

1) One source of noise pollution is noisy machines like mowers, diggers and pneumatic drills, etc.

2) Another is noisy neighbours with their ridiculous stereos, their barking dogs and their hooligan kids.

3) Noise pollution has many harmful effects, the main ones being stress and distraction from work.

4) Noise pollution can be reduced by:
   a) silencing the source   b) insulating homes, buildings or just your ears.

SPECIFIC WAYS OF REDUCING NOISE POLLUTION:

1) Fitting silencers to engines and some sort of mufflers to any other machinery.
2) Sound insulation in buildings: acoustic tiles, curtains, carpets and double glazing.
3) And wearing ear plugs.

If sound travelled in a vacuum — sunny days would be deafening...

Once again the page is broken up into four sections with important numbered points for each. All those numbered points are important. They're all mentioned specifically in the syllabuses so you should expect them to test exactly this stuff in the Exams. Learn and enjoy.

Sound Waves

1) Echoes and Reverberation are due to Sound Being REFLECTED

1) Sound will only be <u>reflected</u> from <u>hard flat surfaces</u>. Things like <u>carpets</u> and <u>curtains</u> act as <u>absorbing surfaces</u> which will <u>absorb</u> sounds rather than reflect them.

2) This is very noticeable in the <u>reverberation</u> in an <u>empty room</u>. A big empty room sounds <u>completely different</u> once you've put carpet and curtains in, and a bit of furniture, because these things absorb the sound quickly and stop it <u>echoing</u> (reverberating) around the room.

2) Amplitude is a Measure of the Energy Carried by Any Wave

1) The <u>greater the amplitude</u>, the <u>more energy</u> the wave carries.

2) In <u>sound</u> this means it'll be <u>louder</u>.

3) <u>Bigger amplitude</u> means a <u>louder sound</u>.

4) With <u>light</u>, a bigger amplitude means it'll be <u>brighter</u>.

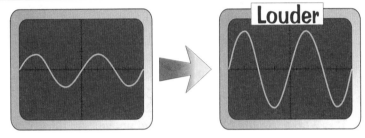

Louder

3) The Frequency of a Sound Wave Determines its Pitch

1) <u>High frequency</u> sound waves sound <u>high pitched</u> like a <u>squeaking mouse</u>.

2) <u>Low frequency</u> sound waves sound <u>low pitched</u> like a <u>mooing cow</u>.

3) <u>Frequency</u> is the number of <u>complete vibrations</u> each second.

4) Common <u>units</u> are <u>kHz</u> (1000 Hz) and <u>MHz</u> (1,000,000 Hz).

5) <u>High frequency</u> (or high pitch) also means <u>shorter wavelength</u>.

6) These <u>CRO traces</u> are <u>very important</u> so make sure you know all about them:

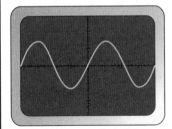 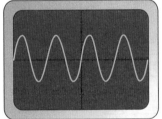 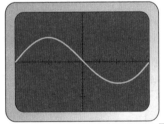 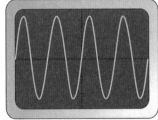

Original Sound   Higher pitched   Lower pitched   Higher pitched and louder

4) Microphones Turn Sound Waves into Electrical Signals

1) The microphone changes the sound wave into a <u>varying electrical current</u>.

2) The <u>variations</u> in the current carry the <u>information</u>.

3) The currents from a <u>microphone</u> are <u>very small</u> and are amplified into <u>much bigger signals</u> by an amplifier.

4) These <u>signals</u> from the microphone can be <u>recorded</u> and played back through <u>speakers</u>.

5) Speakers turn <u>electrical signals</u> into <u>sound waves</u> — <u>exactly the opposite</u> of what a microphone does.

There's more about signals on P. 43.

Amplitude — isn't that a word to say how "chubby" you are...

Another page with four sections, etc. There does seem to be quite a lot of this stuff on boring ordinary waves and sound. But the simple truth is that the more of it you <u>really learn properly</u>, the more marks you'll get in the Exam. You do realise I hope that <u>most Exam questions</u>, even in Physics, simply test whether or not you've <u>learned the basic facts</u>. Just <u>easy marks</u> really.

Ultrasound

Ultrasound *is Sound with a Higher Frequency than We Can Hear*

Electrical devices can be made which produce <u>electrical oscillations</u> of <u>any frequency</u>. These can easily be converted into <u>mechanical vibrations</u> to produce <u>sound</u> waves <u>beyond the range of human hearing</u> (i.e. frequencies above 20 kHz). This is called <u>ultrasound</u> and it has loads of uses:

1) *Industrial Cleaning*

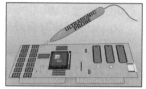

<u>Ultrasound</u> can be used to <u>clean delicate mechanisms</u> without them having to be <u>dismantled</u>. The ultrasound waves can be directed on <u>very precise areas</u> and are extremely effective at <u>removing dirt</u> and other deposits which form on <u>delicate equipment</u>. The alternatives would either <u>damage</u> the equipment or else would require it to be <u>dismantled</u> first.
The same technique is used for <u>cleaning teeth</u>.
Dentists use <u>ultrasonic tools</u> to easily and <u>painlessly</u> remove hard deposits of <u>tartar</u> which build up on teeth and which would lead to <u>gum disease</u>.

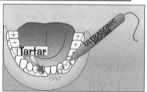

2) *Breaking Down Kidney Stones*

This works like the cleaning method above. An ultrasound beam concentrates <u>high energy shockwaves</u> at the kidney stone and turns it into <u>sand-like particles</u>. These particles then pass out of the body in <u>urine</u>. It's a good method because the patient <u>doesn't need surgery</u> and it's relatively <u>painless</u>.

3) *Industrial Quality Control*

<u>Ultrasound waves</u> can pass through something like a <u>metal casting</u> and whenever they reach a <u>boundary</u> between <u>two different media</u> (like metal and air) some of the wave is <u>reflected back</u> and <u>detected</u>.
The exact <u>timing and distribution</u> of these <u>echoes</u> give <u>detailed information</u> about the <u>internal structure</u>.
The echoes are usually <u>processed by computer</u> to produce a <u>visual display</u> of what the object must be like <u>inside</u>.
If there are cracks where there shouldn't be <u>they'll show up</u>.

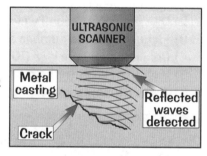

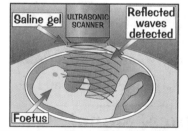

4) *For Pre-Natal Scanning of a Foetus*

This follows the <u>same principle</u> as the industrial quality control. As the ultrasound hits <u>different media</u> some of the sound wave is <u>reflected</u> and these reflected waves are <u>processed by computer</u> to produce a <u>video image</u> of the foetus. No one knows for sure whether ultrasound is safe in all cases but <u>X-rays</u> would definitely be dangerous to the foetus.

5) *Range and Direction Finding — SONAR*

<u>Bats</u> send out <u>high-pitched squeaks</u> (ultrasound) and pick up the <u>reflections</u> with their <u>big ears</u>. Their brains are able to <u>process</u> the reflected signal and turn it into a <u>picture</u> of what's around.
So the bats basically "<u>see</u>" with <u>sound waves</u>, well enough in fact to <u>catch moths</u> in <u>mid-flight</u> in <u>complete darkness</u> — it's a nice trick if you can do it.
The same technique is used for <u>sonar</u> which uses sound waves <u>underwater</u> to detect features in the water and on the seabed. The <u>pattern</u> of the reflections indicates the <u>depth</u> and basic features.

Ultrasound — weren't they a pop group...

Geesh — *another* page on sound and five sections to learn. No numbered points this time though. That means the mini-essay method is going to be a better idea this time. <u>Learn</u> the five headings, then <u>cover the page</u> and <u>scribble a mini-essay</u> for each, with all the diagrams. Enjoy.

Using s = d/t, v = fλ and f = 1/T

They're just formulae, just like all the other formulae, and the same old rules apply (see P. 9).
Mind you, there are a few extra details that go with these wave formulas. Learn them now:

The First Rule: Try and Choose the Right Formula

1) People have way too much difficulty deciding which formula to use.
2) All too often the question starts with "*A wave is travelling...*", and in they leap with "v = fλ".
3) To choose the right formula you have to look for the three quantities mentioned in the question.
4) If the question mentions speed, frequency and wavelength then sure, "v = fλ" is the one to use.
5) But if it has speed, time and distance then "s = d/t" is more the order of the day — wouldn't you say.

Example 1 — Water Ripples

a) *Some ripples travel 55 cm in 5 seconds. Find their speed in cm/s.*
   __ANSWER__: Speed, distance and time are mentioned in the question,
   so you must use "s=d/t":   s = d/t = 55/5 = __11 cm/s__
b) *The wavelength of these waves is found to be 2.2 cm. What is their frequency?*
   __ANSWER__: This time f and λ mentioned, so use "v = fλ", and you'll need this:
   which tells you that f = v/λ = 11 cm/s ÷ 2.2 cm. = __5 Hz__ (It's very cool to use cm/s with cm, s and Hz)

The Second Rule: Watch those Units — The Little Rascals

1) The standard (SI) units involved with waves are: metres, seconds, m/s and Hertz (Hz).

   > Always __CONVERT INTO SI UNITS__ (m, s, Hz, m/s) before you work anything out

2) The trouble is waves often have high frequencies given in kHz or MHz, so make sure you learn this too:

   > 1 kHz (kiloHertz) = 1,000 Hz   1 MHz (1 MegaHertz) = 1,000,000 Hz

3) Wavelengths can also be given in funny units, e.g. km for long wave radio, or cm for sound.
4) There's worse still: The speed of light is 3×10^8 m/s = 300,000,000 m/s. This, along with numbers
   like 900 MHz = 900,000,000 Hz won't fit into a lot of calculators. That leaves you three choices:

   1) Enter the numbers as standard form (3×10^8 and 9×10^8), or...
   2) Cancel three or six noughts off both numbers, (so long as you're dividing them!) or...
   3) Do it entirely without a calculator! (no really, I've seen it done).   Your choice.

Example 2 — Sound

Q) A sound wave travelling in a solid has a frequency of 19 kHz and a wavelength of 12cm. Find its speed.
__ANSWER__: You've got f and λ mentioned, so use "v = fλ". But you must convert the units into SI:
   So, v = f×λ = 19,000 Hz × 0.12 m = __2,280 m/s__ — convert the units and there's no problem.

Example 3 — EM radiation:

Q) A radio wave has a frequency of 92.2 MHz. Find its wavelength. *(The speed of all EM waves is 3×10^8 m/s.)*
__ANSWER__: f and λ are mentioned, so use "v = fλ". Radio waves travel at the speed of light of course.
   Once again, convert the units into SI, but you'll also have to use standard form:
   λ = v/f = 3×10^8 / 92,200,000 = 3×10^8 / 9.22×10^7 = __3.25m__ (There's a few bits to get wrong.)

And finally: Frequency = 1/ Time Period

Q) A wave does 40 complete cycles in 8 seconds. Find its time period, T, and its frequency, f, in Hz.
__ANSWER__: T = time taken for one cycle = 8 secs ÷ 40 = __0.2 s__   f = 1/T = 1 ÷ 0.2 = __5 Hz__

This stuff on formulas is really painful — I mean it MHz...

Sift out the main rules on this page, then cover it up and scribble them down. Then try these:
1) A sound wave has a frequency of 2 500 Hz and a wavelength of 13.2 cm. Find its speed.
2) The radio waves for Radio 4 have a wavelength of 1.5 km. Find their frequency.

Questions on The Speed of Sound

Relative Speeds of Sound and Light

1) <u>Light</u> travels about <u>a million times faster</u> than <u>sound</u>, so you never bother to calculate how long it takes compared to sound. You only work out the time taken for the <u>sound</u> to travel.

2) The <u>formula</u> needed is always the good old <u>s*d*t</u> one for <u>speed, distance and time</u> (see P. 26).

3) When something makes a sound more than about <u>100 m away</u> and you can actually <u>see</u> the action which makes the sound then the effect is quite <u>noticeable</u>. Good examples are:

a) <u>LIVE CRICKET</u> — you hear the "<u>knock</u>" a while after seeing the ball being struck.

b) <u>HAMMERING</u> — you hear the "<u>clang</u>" when the hammer is back up <u>in mid air</u>.

c) <u>STARTING PISTOL</u> — you <u>see the smoke</u> and then <u>hear the bang</u>.

d) <u>JET AIRCRAFT</u> — they're always <u>ahead</u> of where it sounds like they are.

e) <u>THUNDER AND LIGHTNING</u> — the flash of lightning causes the sound of the thunder, and the <u>time interval</u> between the <u>flash</u> and the <u>rumble</u> tells you how far away the lightning is. There's approximately <u>five seconds delay for every mile</u>. (1 mile = 1600 m, ÷ 330 = 4.8 s)

<u>EXAMPLE</u>: *Looking out from his modest office across the Designated (EU Directive 672) Young Persons Recreation Area (i.e. the school yard), the Headmaster saw the five most troublesome and nauseating kids in his school destroying something nice with their horrid hammer. Before acting swiftly, he did take the time to notice that there was a delay of exactly 0.4 seconds between the hammer striking and the sound reaching his shell-like ear. So just how far away were these horrid children? (Sound travels at 330 m/s in air, as you know.)*

<u>ANSWER</u>: The formula we want is of course "Speed = Distance/Time" or "s=d/t". We want to find the distance, d. We already know the time is 0.4 s and the speed of sound in air = 330 m/s Hence d=s×t (from the triangle) This gives: d = 330×0.4 = <u>132m</u>. (That's how far the sound travels in 0.4 secs.) Easy peasy.

Echo Questions — Don't Forget the Factor of Two

1) The <u>big thing</u> to remember with <u>echo questions</u> is that because the sound has to travel <u>both ways</u>, then to get the <u>right answer</u> you'll need to either <u>double something</u> or <u>halve something</u>.

2) Make sure you remember: sound travels at about <u>330 m/s in air</u> and <u>1400 m/s in water</u>. Any echo question is likely to be in air or water and if you have to work out the speed of the sound it's really useful to know what sort of number you should be getting. So for example, if you get 170 m/s for the speed of sound in air then you should realise you've <u>forgotten the factor of two</u> somewhere, and then you can <u>easily go back and sort it</u>.

<u>EXAMPLE</u>: *Having successfully expelled the five most troublesome and nauseating kids from his school, the jubilant Headmaster popped open a bottle of Champagne and heard the echo 0.6 s later from the other side of his modest office. Just how big was this modest office?*

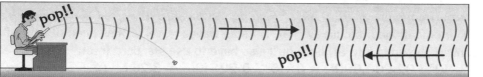

<u>ANSWER</u>: The formula is of course "Speed = Distance/Time" or "s=d/t". We want to find the distance, d. We already know the time, 0.6 s and the speed (of sound in air), hence d=s×t (from triangle) This gives: d = 330×0.6 = <u>198 m</u> But Watch out! <u>Don't forget the factor of two for echo questions</u>: The 0.6 secs is for <u>there and back</u>, so the office is only <u>half</u> that distance, <u>99 m long</u>.

Learn about Echoes and the Factor of Two...Factor of Two...Factor of Two...

<u>Learn</u> the details on this page, then <u>cover it up</u> and <u>scribble them down</u>. Then try these:

1) A man sees the cricketer hit the ball and hears the knock 0.8 s later. How far away is he?

2) A ship sends a sonar signal to the sea bed and detects the echo 0.7 s later. How deep is it?

Reflection: a Property of all Waves

The Ripple Tank is Really Good for Displaying Waves

Learn all these diagrams showing reflection of waves. They could ask you to complete any one of them in the Exam. It can be quite a bit trickier than you think unless you've practised them really well beforehand.

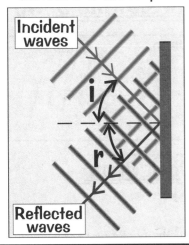

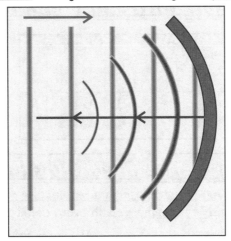

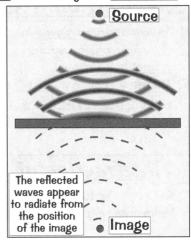

Reflection of Light

1) Reflection of light is what allows us to see objects.
2) When light reflects from an uneven surface such as a piece of paper the light reflects off at all different angles and you get a DIFFUSE REFLECTION.
3) When light reflects from an even surface (smooth and shiny like a mirror) then it's all reflected at the same angle and you get a clear reflection.
4) But don't forget, the LAW OF REFLECTION applies to every reflected ray:

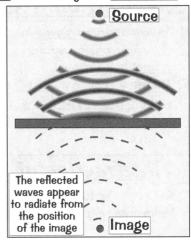

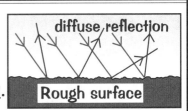

Angle of INCIDENCE = Angle of REFLECTION

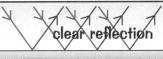

Reflection In a Plane Mirror — How to Locate The Image

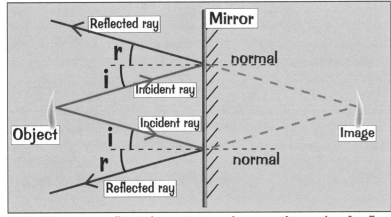

You need to be able to reproduce this entire diagram of how an image is formed in a PLANE MIRROR.
Learn these three important points:

1) The image is the same size as the object.
2) It is AS FAR BEHIND the mirror as the object is in front.
3) It's formed from diverging rays, which means it's a virtual image.

1) To draw any reflected ray, just make sure the angle of reflection, r, equals the angle of incidence, i.
2) Note that these two angles are ALWAYS defined between the ray itself and the dotted NORMAL.
3) Don't ever label them as the angle between the ray and the surface. Definitely uncool.

Learn reflection thoroughly — try to look at it from all sides...

First make sure you can draw all those diagrams from memory. Then make sure you've learnt the rest well enough to answer typical mean Exam questions like these: "Explain why you can see a piece of paper" "What is diffuse reflection?" "Why is the image in a plane mirror virtual?"

Refraction: a Property of all Waves

1) <u>Refraction</u> is when waves <u>change direction</u> as they <u>enter a different</u> medium.
2) This is caused <u>entirely</u> by the <u>change in speed</u> of the waves.
3) It also causes the <u>wavelength</u> to change, but remember that the <u>frequency</u> does <u>not</u> change.

1) Refraction is Shown by Waves in a Ripple Tank Slowing Down

1) The waves travel <u>slower</u> in <u>shallower water</u>, causing <u>refraction</u> as shown.
2) There's a <u>change in direction</u>, and a <u>change in wavelength</u> but <u>NO change in frequency</u>.

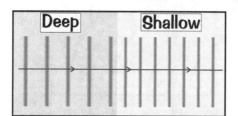

2) Refraction of Light — The Good Old Glass Block Demo

You can't fail to remember the old "<u>ray of light through a rectangular glass block</u>" trick.
Make sure you can draw this diagram <u>from memory</u>, with every detail <u>perfect</u>.

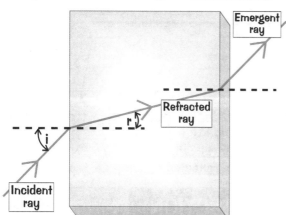

Emergent ray

Refracted ray

Incident ray

1) <u>Take careful note</u> of the positions of the <u>normals</u> and the <u>exact positions</u> of the angles of <u>incidence</u> and <u>refraction</u> (and note it's the angle of <u>refraction</u> — not <u>reflection</u>).
2) Most important of all, remember <u>which way</u> the ray <u>bends</u>.
3) The ray bends <u>towards the normal</u> as it enters the <u>denser medium</u>, and <u>away</u> from the normal as it <u>emerges</u> into the <u>less dense</u> medium.
4) Try to <u>visualise</u> the shape of the <u>wiggle</u> in the diagram — that can be easier than remembering the rule in words.

3) Refraction Is always Caused By the Waves Changing Speed

1) When waves <u>slow down</u> they bend <u>towards</u> the normal.
2) When <u>light</u> enters <u>glass</u> it <u>slows down</u> to about <u>2/3 of its normal speed</u> (in air) i.e. it slows down to about 2×10^8 m/s rather than 3×10^8 m/s.
3) When waves hit the boundary <u>along a normal</u>, i.e. at <u>exactly 90°</u>, then there will be <u>no change</u> in direction. That's pretty important to remember, because they often <u>sneak it into a question</u> somewhere. There'll still be a change in <u>speed</u> and <u>wavelength</u>, though.
4) <u>Some</u> light is also <u>reflected</u> when light hits a <u>different medium</u> such as glass.

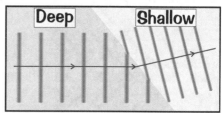

Normal incidence so no bending

Ray slowed to 2/3 speed wavelength reduced

4) Sound Waves also Refract But it's Hard to Spot

<u>Sound waves</u> will also refract (change direction) as they enter <u>different media</u>. However, since sound waves are always <u>spreading out so much</u>, the change in direction is <u>hard to spot</u> under normal circumstances. (They bend <u>away</u> from the normal because, unlike light, they're <u>speeding up</u>.)
Just remember, <u>sound waves do refract</u>, OK?

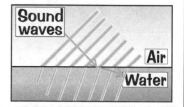

Sound waves

Air

Water

Revise Refraction — but don't let it slow you down...

The first thing you've gotta do is make sure you can spot the difference between the words <u>refraction</u> and <u>reflection</u>. After that you need to <u>learn all this stuff about refraction</u> — so you know exactly what it is. Make sure you know all those <u>diagrams</u> inside out. <u>Cover and scribble.</u>

Refraction: Two Special Cases

Dispersion Produces Rainbows

1) <u>Different colours of light</u> are <u>refracted</u> by <u>different amounts</u>.

2) This is because they travel at <u>slightly different speeds</u> in any given <u>medium</u>.

3) A <u>prism</u> can be used to make the different colours of white light emerge at <u>different angles</u>.

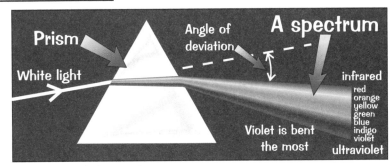

Prism **A spectrum**
Angle of deviation
White light
Violet is bent the most
infrared
red
orange
yellow
green
blue
indigo
violet
ultraviolet

4) This produces a <u>spectrum</u> showing all the colours of the <u>rainbow</u>. This effect is called <u>DISPERSION</u>.

5) You need to know that <u>red light</u> is refracted the <u>least</u> — and <u>violet</u> is refracted the <u>most</u>.

6) Also know the <u>order of colours</u> in between: <u>Red Orange Yellow Green Blue Indigo Violet</u>

   which is remembered by: Richard Of York Gave Battle In Vain

   They may well test whether you can put them correctly into the diagram.

7) Also learn where <u>infrared</u> and <u>ultraviolet</u> light would appear if you could detect them.

Total Internal Reflection and The Critical Angle

1) This <u>only happens</u> when <u>light</u> is <u>coming out</u> of something <u>dense</u> like <u>glass</u> or <u>water</u> or <u>perspex</u>.

2) If the <u>angle</u> is <u>shallow enough</u> the ray <u>won't come out at all</u>, but it <u>reflects</u> back into the glass (or whatever). This is called <u>total internal reflection</u> because <u>all</u> of the light <u>reflects back in</u>.

3) You definitely need to learn this set of <u>three diagrams</u> which show the three conditions:

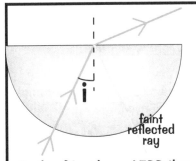

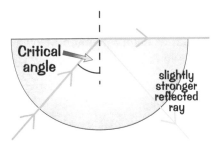

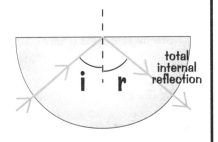

faint reflected ray

Critical angle
slightly stronger reflected ray

total internal reflection

<u>Angle of Incidence LESS than the Critical Angle.</u>
Most of the light <u>passes through</u> into the air but a <u>little</u> bit of it is <u>internally reflected</u>.

<u>Angle of Incidence EQUAL TO the Critical Angle.</u>
The emerging ray comes out <u>along the surface</u>. There's quite a bit of <u>internal reflection</u>.

<u>Angle of Incidence GREATER than the Critical Angle.</u>
<u>No light comes out.</u>
It's <u>all</u> internally reflected, i.e. <u>total internal reflection</u>.

1) The <u>Critical Angle</u> for <u>glass</u> is about 42°. This is <u>very handy</u> because it means <u>45° angles</u> can be used to get <u>total internal reflection</u> as in the <u>prisms</u> in the <u>binoculars</u> and <u>periscope</u> shown on the next page.

2) In *diamond* the <u>Critical Angle</u> is much <u>lower</u> — about <u>24°</u>. This is the reason why diamonds <u>sparkle</u> so much, because there are lots of <u>internal reflections</u>.

Revision — sure it's Critical, but it's not a prism sentence...

First and foremost make sure you can <u>scribble all the diagrams</u> down with all the details. Then <u>scribble a mini-essay</u> for each topic, jotting down everything you can remember. Then check back and see what you <u>missed</u>. Then <u>learn the stuff you forgot</u> and <u>try again</u>. Ahh... such fun.

Uses of Total Internal Reflection

Total Internal Reflection is used in binoculars, periscopes and bicycle reflectors. All three use 45° prisms.

Binoculars

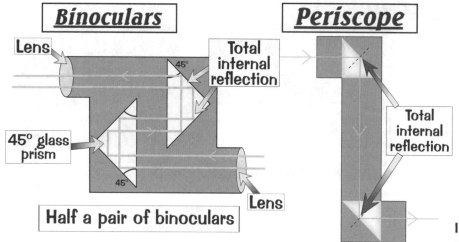

Lens

Total internal reflection

45°

45° glass prism

45°

Lens

Half a pair of binoculars

Periscope

Total internal reflection

Reflectors

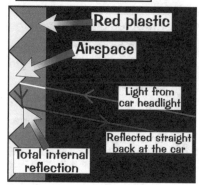

Red plastic

Airspace

Light from car headlight

Reflected straight back at the car

Total internal reflection

In the case of the binoculars and periscope, the prisms give slightly better reflection than a mirror would and they're also easier to hold accurately in place. Learn the exact positioning of the prisms. They could ask you to complete a diagram of binoculars or a periscope and unless you've practised beforehand you'll find it pretty tricky to draw the prisms in properly.

In the bicycle reflectors the prisms work cleverly by sending the light back in exactly the opposite direction that it came from (as shown in the diagram). This means that whoever shines the light gets a strong reflection straight back at their eyes.

Optical Fibres — Communications and Endoscopes

1) Optical fibres can carry information over long distances by repeated total internal reflections.
2) Optical communications have several advantages over electrical signals in wires:
   a) the signal doesn't need boosting as often.
   b) a cable of the same diameter can carry a lot more information.
   c) the signals cannot be tapped into, or suffer interference from electrical sources.
3) Normally no light whatever would be lost at each reflection. However some light is lost due to imperfections in the surface, so it still needs boosting every few km.

The fibre must be narrow enough to keep the angles above the critical angle, as shown, so the fibre mustn't be bent too sharply anywhere.

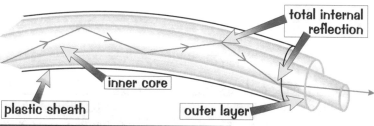

total internal reflection

inner core

plastic sheath

outer layer

Endoscopes are Used to Look Inside People

This is a narrow bunch of optical fibres with a lens system at each end. Another bunch of optical fibres carries light down inside to see with.
The image is displayed as a full colour moving image on a TV screen. Real impressive stuff. This means they can do operations without cutting big holes in people. This was never possible before optical fibres.

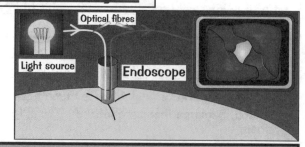

Optical fibres

Light source

Endoscope

Total Internal Reflection — sounds like a Government Inquiry...

Three sections to learn here, with diagrams for each. They always have at least one of these applications of total internal reflection in the Exam. Learn them all. None of this is difficult — but just make sure you've got all those little picky details firmly fastened inside your head.

Digital and Analogue Signals

You've got to learn the <u>two</u> different ways of transmitting information. Life would be pretty dull without signals — no phones, no computers, even groovy digital watches wouldn't exist.

Information is Converted Into Signals

1) Information (eg: sound, speech, pictures) is converted into <u>electrical signals</u> before it's transmitted.
2) It's then sent long distances down <u>cables</u>, like telephone calls or internet, or carried on <u>EM waves</u>, like radio or TV.
3) Information can also be sent down <u>optical fibres</u> by converting it into <u>visible light</u> or <u>infrared</u> signals.

Analogue Varies But Digital's Either On or Off

1) The <u>amplitude</u> and <u>frequency</u> of analogue signals <u>vary continuously</u> like in sound waves. Parts of an analogue signal have <u>any</u> value in a range.
2) Dimmer switches, thermometers, speedometers and old fashioned watches are all <u>analogue</u> devices.
3) Digital signals are <u>coded pulses</u> — they have <u>one</u> of only <u>two</u> values: on or off, true or false, 0 or 1...
4) On/off switches, digital clocks and digital meters are <u>digital</u> devices.

Analogue

Digital

pulses

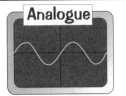
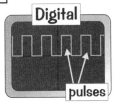

Signals Have to Be Amplified

Both digital and analogue signals <u>weaken</u> as they travel so they need to be <u>amplified</u> along their route. They also pick up <u>random disturbances</u>, called <u>noise</u>.

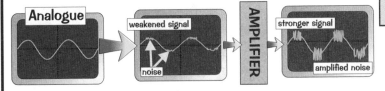

Analogue | weakened signal | noise | AMPLIFIER | stronger signal | amplified noise

Analogue Signals Lose Quality

Each time it's amplified, the analogue signal gets <u>less and less</u> like the original. The different frequencies in it <u>weaken differently</u> at different times — when the signal is amplified, the <u>differences and noise</u> are amplified too.

Digital Signals Stay The Same

Noise is usually <u>low amplitude</u> so it's just ignored — it's amplified as OFF. Even a weak signal will still be picked up as an ON pulse so it's amplified as ON. The signal <u>stays exactly the same</u> as the original.

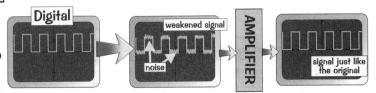

Digital | weakened signal | noise | AMPLIFIER | signal just like the original

Digital Signals are Far Better Quality

1) Digital signals <u>don't change</u> while they're being transmitted. This makes them <u>higher quality</u> — the information transmitted is the <u>same</u> as the original.
2) <u>Loads more information</u> can be sent as digital signals compared to analogue (in a certain time). Many digital signals can be transmitted at once by a clever way of <u>overlapping</u> them on the <u>same</u> cable or EM wave — but you don't need to learn <i>how</i> they do it, phew.

Pulses are higher quality — especially those nice Heinz ones...

This stuff follows on neatly from optical fibres so you can bet you'll get a question on it. Make sure you know the <u>differences</u> between digital and analogue signals and <u>why</u> digital ones are better. Learn all the details, then turn the book over and scribble them all down.

Diffraction: a Property of all Waves

This word sounds a lot more technical than it really is.

Diffraction is Just the "Spreading Out" of Waves

All waves tend to spread out at the edges when they pass through a gap or past an object. Instead of saying that the wave "spreads out" or "bends" round a corner you should say that it DIFFRACTS around the corner. It's as easy as that. That's all diffraction means.

A Wave Spreads More if it Passes Through a Narrow Gap

The ripple tank shows this effect quite nicely. The same effect applies to light and sound waves too.

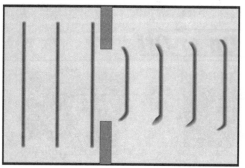 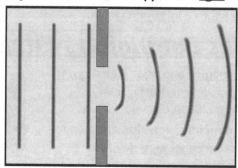 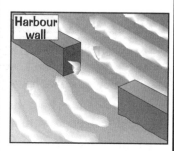

1) A "narrow" gap is one which is about the same size as the wavelength or less.
2) Obviously then, the question of whether a gap is "narrow" or not depends on the wave in question. What may be a narrow gap for a water wave will be a huge gap for a light wave.
3) It should be obvious then, that the longer the wavelength of a wave the more it will diffract.

Sounds Always Diffract Quite a Lot, Because λ is Quite Big

1) Most sounds have wavelengths in air of around 0.1 m, which is quite long.

2) This means they spread out round corners so you can still hear people even when you can't see them directly (the sound usually reflects off walls too which also helps).

3) Higher frequency sounds will have shorter wavelengths and so they won't diffract as much, which is why things sound more "muffled" when you hear them from round corners.

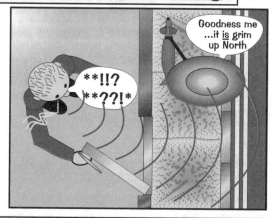

Long Wavelength Radio Waves Diffract Easily Over Hills and into Buildings:

Shorter wavelength TV and FM radio do not diffract very much

Long wavelength radio waves diffract

These houses will get reception of long wave radio, but not TV or FM radio

Visible Light on the other hand...

has a very short wavelength, and it'll only diffract with a very narrow slit:

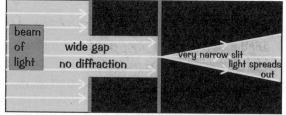

beam of light — wide gap no diffraction — very narrow slit light spreads out

This spreading or diffraction of light (and radio waves) is strong evidence for the wave nature of light.

Diffraction — it can drive you round the bend...

People usually don't know much about diffraction, mainly because there are so few lab demos you can do to show it, and there's also very little to say about it — about one page's worth, in fact. The thing is though, if you just learn this page properly, then you'll know all you need to.

The Electromagnetic Spectrum

The Seven Types of EM Wave Travel At the Same Speed

The properties of electromagnetic waves (EM waves) change as the frequency (or wavelength) changes.
We split them into seven basic types as shown below.
These EM waves form a continuous spectrum so the different regions do actually merge into each other.

RADIO WAVES	MICRO WAVES	INFRA RED	VISIBLE LIGHT	ULTRA VIOLET	X-RAYS	GAMMA RAYS
$1m-10^4 m$	$10^{-2} m$ (3cm)	$10^{-5} m$ (0.01mm)	$10^{-7}m$	$10^{-8}m$	$10^{-10} m$	$10^{-12} m$

Our eyes can only detect a very narrow range of EM waves which are the ones we call (visible) light.
All EM waves travel at exactly the same speed as light in a vacuum, and pretty much the same speed as light in other media like glass or water — though this is always slower than their speed in vacuum.

As the Wavelength Changes, So Do The Properties

1) As the wavelength of EM radiation changes, its interaction with matter changes. In particular, the way any EM wave is absorbed, reflected or transmitted by any given substance depends entirely on its wavelength — that's the whole point of these three pages of course.
2) As a rule the EM waves at each end of the spectrum tend to be able to pass through material, whilst those nearer the middle are absorbed.
3) Also, the ones at the top end (high frequency, short wavelength) tend to be the most dangerous, whilst those lower down are generally harmless.
4) When any EM radiation is absorbed it can cause two effects:
   a) Heating   b) Creation of a tiny alternating current with the same frequency as the radiation.
5) You need to know all the details that follow about all the different parts of the EM spectrum:

Radio Waves are Used Mainly For Communications

1) Radio Waves are used mainly for communication and, perhaps more importantly, for controlling model aeroplanes.
2) Both TV and FM Radio use short wavelength radio waves of about 1m wavelength.
3) To receive these wavelengths you need to be more or less in direct sight of the transmitter, because they will not bend (diffract) over hills or travel very far through buildings.

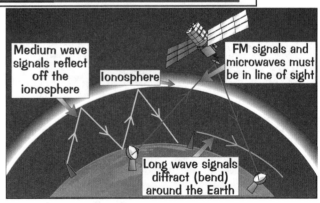

Medium wave signals reflect off the ionosphere

Ionosphere

FM signals and microwaves must be in line of sight

Long wave signals diffract (bend) around the Earth

4) Long Wave radio on the other hand has wavelengths of about 1 km and these waves will bend over the surface of the Earth and also diffract into tunnels and all sorts.
5) Medium Wave radio signals which have wavelengths of about 300 m can be received long distances from the transmitter because they are reflected from the ionosphere, which is an electrically charged layer in the Earth's upper atmosphere. Mind you, these signals are always so fuzzy they're not worth listening to anyway (in my humble opinion).

The spectrum — isn't that something kinda rude in Biology...

There are lots of details on this page that you definitely need to know. The top diagram is an absolute must — they usually give it you with one or two missing labels to be filled in. Learn the three sections on this page then scribble a mini-essay for each one to see what you know.

Microwaves and Infrared

Microwaves Are Used For Cooking and Satellite Signals

1) Microwaves have two main uses: cooking food and satellite transmissions.

2) These two applications use two different frequencies of microwaves.

3) Satellite transmissions use a frequency which passes easily through the Earth's atmosphere, including clouds, which seems pretty sensible.

4) The frequency used for cooking, on the other hand is one which is readily absorbed by water molecules. This is how a microwave oven works. The microwaves pass easily into the food and are then absorbed by the water molecules and turn into heat inside the food.

5) Microwaves can therefore be dangerous because they can be absorbed by living tissue and the heat will damage or kill the cells causing a sort of "cold burn".

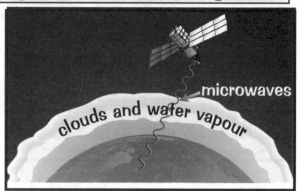

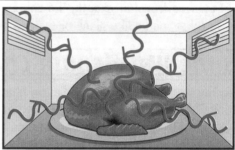

Infrared Radiation — Night-Vision and Remote Controls

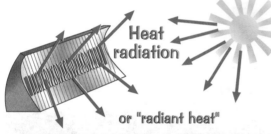

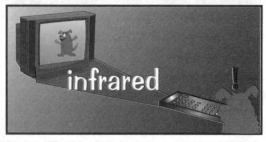

1) Infrared (or IR) is otherwise known as heat radiation. This is given out by all hot objects and you feel it on your skin as radiant heat. Infrared is readily absorbed by all materials and causes heating.

2) Radiant heaters (i.e. those that glow red) use infrared radiation, including toasters and grills.

3) Infrared is also used for night-vision equipment. This works by detecting the heat radiation given off by all objects, even in the dark of night, and turning it into an electrical signal which is displayed on a screen as a clear picture. The hotter an object is, the brighter it appears. Police and the military use this to spot miscreants running away, like you've seen on TV.

4) Infrared is also used for all the remote controls of TVs and videos. It's ideal for sending harmless signals over short distances without interfering with other radio frequencies (like the TV channels).

I want a remote control / grill combo — to cook pizzas from my armchair...

Each part of the EM spectrum is different, and you definitely need to know all the details about each type of radiation. These are just the kind of things they'll test in your Exams. Do mini-essays for microwaves and IR. Then check to see how you did. Then try again... and again...

Visible and UV Light, X-Rays and γ-Rays

Visible light is Used To See With and In Optical Fibres

1) Visible light is pretty useful. We use it for <u>seeing</u> with for one thing.
2) It's also used in <u>Optical Fibre Digital Communications</u> which is the best use by far for your answer <u>in the Exam</u>.
3) You could say that a use of it is in <u>endoscopes</u> for seeing inside a patient's body, but let's face it, where do you draw the line? — <u>microscopes</u>, <u>telescopes</u>, <u>kaleidoscopes</u>, pretend telescopes made of old toilet rolls, seeing in the dark (torch, lights, glow stars etc) and, perhaps most importantly, for controlling model aeroplanes.

Ultraviolet Light Causes Skin Cancer

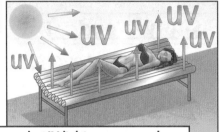

1) <u>Skin cancer</u> is caused by spending <u>too much time</u> soaking up the UV rays from the <u>Sun</u>.
2) It makes you <u>tan</u>. <u>Sunbeds</u> give out fewer UV rays than the Sun but they're still <u>harmful</u>.
3) <u>Tanned or darker skin</u> protects against UV rays. It <u>stops</u> them reaching more <u>vulnerable skin tissues</u> deeper down.
4) <u>Special coatings</u> which <u>absorb UV light</u> and then <u>give out visible light</u> instead are used to coat the inside of <u>fluorescent tubes</u> and lamps.
5) UV is also useful for <u>hidden security marks</u> which are written in special ink that can only be seen with an ultraviolet light.

Note: only UV light causes sunburn

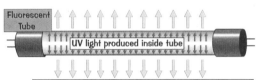

Coating on glass absorbs UV and emits visible light

X-Rays Are Used in Hospitals, but are Pretty Dangerous

1) <u>Radiographers</u> in <u>hospitals</u> take <u>X-ray photographs</u> of people to see whether they have any <u>broken bones</u>.
2) X-rays pass <u>easily through flesh</u> but not through <u>denser material</u> like <u>bones</u> or <u>metal</u>.
3) X-rays can cause <u>cancer</u>, so radiographers wear <u>lead aprons</u> and stand behind a <u>lead screen</u> or <u>leave the room</u> to keep their <u>exposure</u> to X-rays to a <u>minimum</u>.

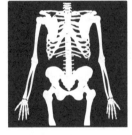

The <u>brighter bits</u> are where <u>fewer X-rays</u> get through. This is a <u>negative image</u>. The plate starts off <u>all white</u>.

Gamma Rays Treat Cancer Without Surgery

1) Gamma rays are used to kill <u>harmful bacteria</u> to keep food <u>fresher for longer</u> and <u>sterilise medical instruments</u>.
2) In <u>high doses</u>, gamma rays, X-rays and UV rays can <u>kill normal cells</u>.
3) In <u>lower doses</u>, these three types of EM waves can cause normal cells to become <u>cancerous</u>. Eek.
4) If the dose is just right, gamma rays can be used to treat cancer <u>without surgery</u> because they <u>kill cancer cells</u>.

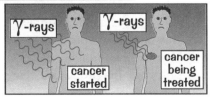

Radiographers are like Teachers — they can see right through you...

Here are the other four parts of the EM spectrum for you to learn. Ace, isn't it. At least there are some groovy diagrams to help relieve the tedium. On this page there are four sections. Do a <u>mini-essay</u> for each section, then <u>check</u>, <u>re-learn</u>, <u>re-scribble</u>, <u>re-check</u>, etc. etc.

Seismic Waves

Seismic Waves Are Caused By Earthquakes

1) We can only drill about 10 km or so into the crust of the Earth, which is not very far, so seismic waves are really the only way of investigating the inner structure.
2) When there's an Earthquake somewhere the shock waves travel out from it and we detect them all over the surface of the planet using seismographs.
3) The time it takes for the two different types of shock wave to reach each seismograph is measured.
4) Seismologists also note the parts of the Earth which don't receive the shock waves at all.
5) From this information you can work out all sorts of stuff about the inside of the Earth as shown below:

S-Waves and P-Waves Take Different Paths

P-Waves are Longitudinal

P-waves travel through both solids and liquids. They travel faster than S-waves.

S-Waves are TranSverSe

S-waves will only travel through solids. They are slower than P-waves.

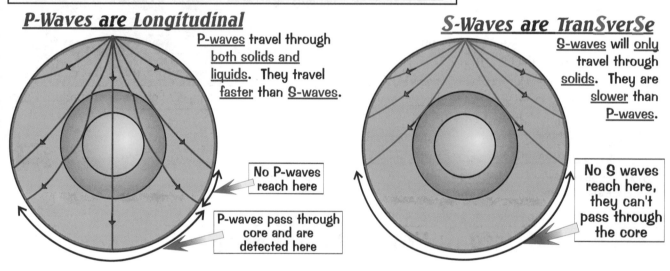

No P-waves reach here

P-waves pass through core and are detected here

No S waves reach here, they can't pass through the core

The Seismograph Results Tell Us What's Down There

1) About halfway through the Earth, there's an abrupt change in direction of both types of wave. This indicates that there's a sudden change in properties at that point — the core.
2) The fact that S-waves are not detected in the shadow of this core tells us that it's liquid.
3) It's also found that P-waves travel slightly faster through the middle of the core, which strongly suggests that there's a solid inner core.
4) Note that S-waves do travel through the mantle, which shows that it's solid. It only melts to form magma in small 'hot spots'.

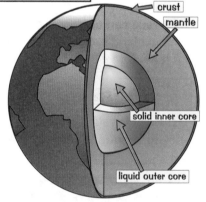

crust
mantle
solid inner core
liquid outer core

The Paths Curve with Increasing Depth

1) The waves change speed as the properties of the mantle and core change.
2) This change in speed causes the waves to change direction — which is refraction, of course.
3) Most of the time the waves change speed gradually, resulting in a curved path.
4) But when the properties change suddenly, the speed will change abruptly, and the path will have a kink.

Seismic Waves — they reveal the terrible trembling truth...

This section just keeps getting more exciting. Once again there are four main sections to learn. Learn the headings first, then try scribbling down all the details for each heading, including the diagrams. Remember that S-waves are tranSverSe — so P-waves must be the longitudinal ones.

The Earth's Structure

Crust, Mantle, Outer and Inner Core

1) The crust is very thin (well, about 20km or so!).

2) The mantle extends almost halfway to the centre of the Earth.

3) It's got all the properties of a solid but it can flow very slowly.

4) The core is just over half the Earth's radius.

5) The core is made of iron and nickel. This is where the Earth's magnetic field originates.

6) The core is solid in the middle and liquid at the edge.

7) Radioactive decay creates a lot of the heat inside the Earth.

8) This heat causes the convection currents which cause the plates of the Earth's surface to move.

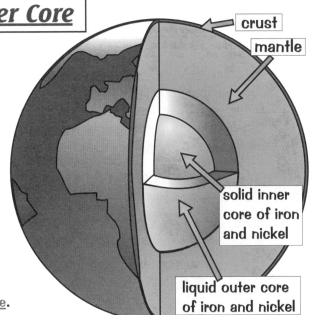

crust
mantle
solid inner core of iron and nickel
liquid outer core of iron and nickel

Big Clues: Seismic Waves, Magnetism and Meteorites

1) We can tell how dense the Earth is by measuring seismic waves and the Earth's motion. We find that the core is much too dense to be made out of rock.

2) Meteorites which crash to Earth are often made of iron and nickel.

3) If the core of the Earth were made of iron and nickel it would explain a lot: iron and nickel are both about the right density, and being metals, this would help explain the Earth's magnetic field (it's like a giant electromagnet).

4) Also, by following the paths of seismic waves as they travel through the Earth, we can tell that there is a change to liquid about halfway through the Earth.

5) There must be a liquid outer core of iron and nickel. The seismic waves also indicate a solid inner core. See how very easy it all is when you know.

The Earth's Surface is made up of Large Plates of Rock

1) These plates are like big rafts that float across the mantle.

2) The map shows the edges of these plates. As they move, the continents move too.

3) Most of the plates are moving at a speed of about 1 cm or 2 cm per year.

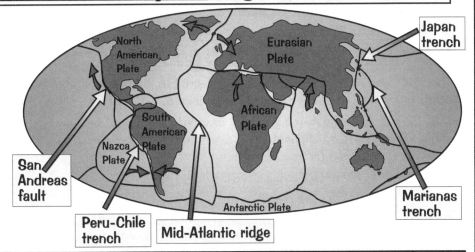

North American Plate
Eurasian Plate
Japan trench
South American Plate
African Plate
Nazca Plate
San Andreas fault
Antarctic Plate
Peru-Chile trench
Mid-Atlantic ridge
Marianas trench

Try Telling that lot to the Spanish Inquisition...

More nice easy stuff. That means it's nice easy marks in the Exam too. They do put easy stuff in, just so that everyone gets at least some marks. Just make sure you learn all the details. There's nothing dafter than missing easy marks. Cover the page and check you know it all.

Evidence for Plate Tectonics

The old theory was that all the features of the Earth's surface, e.g. mountains, were due to shrinkage of the crust as it cooled. In the Exam they may well ask you about that, and then they'll ask you for evidence in favour of plate tectonics as a better theory. Learn and prosper:

1) Jigsaw Fit — the supercontinent "Pangaea"

a) There's a very obvious jigsaw fit between Africa and South America.
b) The other continents can also be fitted in without too much trouble.
c) It's widely believed that they once all formed a single land mass, now called Pangaea.

2) Matching Fossils in Africa and South America

a) Identical plant fossils of the same age have been found in rocks in South Africa, Australia, Antarctica, India and South America, which strongly suggests they were all joined once upon a time.

b) Animal fossils support the theory too. There are identical fossils of a freshwater crocodile found in both Brazil and South Africa. It certainly didn't swim across.

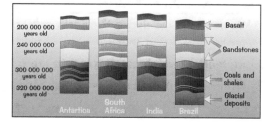

Identical fossils of the same freshwater crocodile found in both South America and South Africa

3) Identical Rock Sequences

a) When rock strata of similar ages are studied in various countries they show remarkable similarity.

b) This is strong evidence that these countries were joined together when the rocks formed.

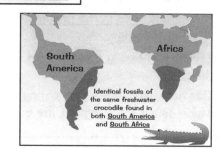

4) Living Creatures: The Earthworm

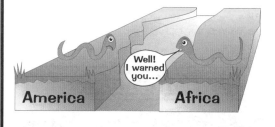

a) There are various living creatures found in both America and Africa.
b) One such beasty is a particular earthworm which is found living at the tip of South America and the tip of South Africa.
c) Most likely it travelled across ever so slowly on the big raft we now call America.

Wegener's Theory of Crustal Movement

This stuff was noticed hundreds of years ago, but nobody really believed that the continents could once have actually been joined.

In 1915, a chap called Alfred Wegener proposed his theory of "continental drift" saying that they had definitely been joined and that they were slowly drifting apart. This wasn't accepted for two reasons:
a) he couldn't give a convincing reason why it happened,
b) he wasn't a qualified geologist.

Only in the 1960s with fossil evidence and the magnetic pattern (see P.52) from the mid-Atlantic ridge was the theory widely accepted.

Learn about Plate Tectonics — but don't get carried away...

Five bits of evidence which support the theory that there are big plates of rock moving about. Learn all five well enough to be able to answer a question like this: "Describe evidence which supports the theory of Plate Tectonics" (5 marks). Learn, cover, scribble, etc...

Plate Boundaries

At the <u>boundaries</u> between tectonic plates there's usually <u>trouble</u> like <u>volcanoes</u> or <u>earthquakes</u>.
There are <u>three</u> different ways that plates interact: <u>Colliding</u>, <u>separating</u> or <u>sliding</u> past each other.

Oceanic and Continental Plates Colliding: The Andes

1) The <u>oceanic plate</u> is always <u>forced</u> <u>underneath</u> the continental plate.

2) This is called a <u>subduction zone</u>.

3) As the oceanic crust is pushed down it <u>melts</u> and <u>pressure builds up</u> due to all the melting rock.

4) This <u>molten rock</u> finds its way to the <u>surface</u> and <u>volcanoes</u> form.

5) There are also <u>earthquakes</u> as the two plates slowly <u>grind</u> past each other.

6) A <u>deep trench</u> forms on the ocean floor where the <u>oceanic plate</u> is being <u>forced down</u>.

7) The <u>continental</u> crust <u>crumples</u> and <u>folds</u> forming <u>mountains</u> at the coast.

8) The classic example of all this is the <u>west coast of South America</u> where the <u>Andes mountains</u> are. That region has <u>all the features</u>:

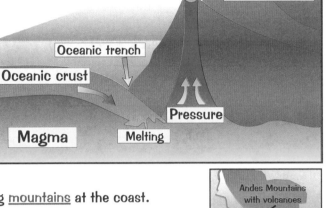

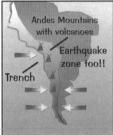

Volcanoes, earthquakes, an oceanic trench and mountains.

Two Continental Plates Collide: The Himalayas

1) The <u>two continental plates</u> meet <u>head on</u>, neither one being subducted.

2) Any <u>sediment layers</u> lying between the two continent masses get <u>squeezed</u> between them.

3) These sediment layers inevitably start <u>crumpling</u> <u>and folding</u> and soon form into <u>big mountains</u>.

4) The <u>Himalayan mountains</u> are the classic case of this.

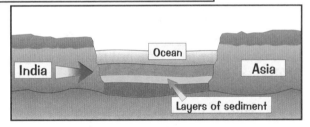

5) <u>India</u> actually <u>broke away</u> from the side of Africa and <u>piled</u> into the bottom of <u>Asia</u>, and is <u>still</u> doing so, <u>pushing the Himalayas up</u> as it goes.

6) <u>Mount Everest</u> is there and is <u>getting higher</u> by a few cm every year as India continues to push up into the continent of Asia.

Another page to learn — don't make a mountain out of it...

<u>Make sure you learn all these diagrams</u> — they summarise all the information in the text.
They may well ask you for examples in the Exam, so make sure you know the two different
kinds of situation that the Andes and the Himalayas actually represent. <u>Cover and scribble...</u>

Plate Boundaries

Sea Floor Spreading: The mid-Atlantic Ridge

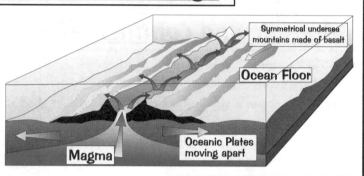

Symmetrical undersea mountains made of basalt

Ocean Floor

Oceanic Plates moving apart

Magma

1) When tectonic plates move <u>apart</u>, magma <u>rises up</u> to fill the gap and produces <u>new crust</u> made of <u>basalt</u> (of course). Sometimes it comes out with <u>great force</u> producing <u>undersea volcanoes</u>.

2) The <u>MID-ATLANTIC RIDGE</u> runs the <u>whole length</u> of the Atlantic and actually cuts through the middle of <u>Iceland</u>, which is why they have <u>hot underground water</u>.

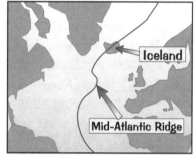

Iceland

Mid-Atlantic Ridge

3) As the magma rises up through the gap, it forms <u>ridges</u> and <u>underwater mountains</u>.

4) These form a <u>symmetrical pattern</u> either side of the ridge, providing strong <u>evidence</u> for the theory of <u>continental drift</u>.

5) However the most <u>compelling</u> evidence comes from the <u>magnetic orientation</u> of the rocks.

6) As the <u>liquid magma</u> erupts out of the gap, the <u>iron particles</u> in the rocks tend to <u>align themselves</u> with the <u>Earth's magnetic field</u> and as it cools they <u>set</u> in position.

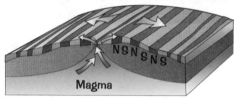

N S N S N S

Magma

7) Every half million years or so the Earth's magnetic field tends to <u>swap direction</u>.

8) This means the rock on <u>either side of the ridge</u> has bands of <u>alternate magnetic polarity</u>.

9) This pattern is found to be <u>symmetrical</u> either side of the ridge.

Plates Sliding Past Each Other: San Francisco

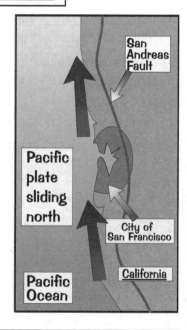

San Andreas Fault

Pacific plate sliding north

City of San Francisco

California

Pacific Ocean

1) Sometimes the plates are just <u>sliding past each other</u>.

2) The best known example of this is the <u>San Andreas Fault</u> in California.

3) A narrow strip of the coastline is <u>sliding north</u> at about <u>7cm a year</u>.

4) Big plates of rock <u>don't glide smoothly</u> past each other.

5) They <u>catch</u> on each other and as the <u>forces build up</u> they suddenly <u>lurch</u>.

6) This <u>sudden lurching</u> only lasts <u>a few seconds</u> — but it'll bring buildings down, no problem.

7) The city of <u>San Francisco</u> sits <u>astride</u> this fault line. (They didn't know when they built it!)

8) The city was <u>destroyed</u> by an earthquake in <u>1906</u> and hit by another quite serious one in <u>1991</u>. They could have another one <u>any time</u>.

9) In <u>earthquake zones</u> they try to build <u>earthquake-proof buildings</u> which are designed to withstand a bit of shaking.

10) Earthquakes usually cause <u>much greater devastation</u> in <u>poorer countries</u> where they may have <u>overcrowded cities</u>, <u>poorly constructed buildings</u>, and <u>inadequate rescue services</u>.

11) It's impossible to accurately predict <u>when</u> an earthquake will occur because there's loads of reasons <u>why</u> they happen and it's hard to <u>take measurements</u>.

Earthquakes — learn the shocking truth...

<u>Let me remind you</u> of the glories of the <u>mini-essay method</u>. You read the stuff and try and learn it. Then you cover the page and scribble yourself a mini-essay on each topic. Then you look back and see what stuff you missed. Then you try again, and again — until you get it all.

Revision Summary for Section Three

One thing's for sure — there are loads of easy facts to learn about waves. Of course there are still some bits which need thinking about, but really, most of it is fairly easy stuff which just needs learning. Don't forget, this book contains all the important information they've specifically mentioned in the syllabus, and this is precisely the stuff they're going to test you on in the Exams. You must practise these questions over and over again until they're easy.

1) Sketch transverse and longtitudinal waves. Define them and give examples of both types.
2) Define frequency and time period for a wave. Give three examples of waves carrying energy.
3) Write down the speed of sound in air. Describe the bell jar experiment. What does it demonstrate?
4) Sketch graphs of normal and damaged hearing. Write down three ways of reducing noise pollution.
5) What's the connection between amplitude and the energy carried by a wave?
6) What effect does greater amplitude have on a) sound waves b) light waves?
7) What's the relationship between frequency and pitch for a sound wave?
8) Sketch CRO screens showing higher and lower pitch and quiet and loud sounds.
9) What is ultrasound? Give full details of five applications of ultrasound.
10) What are the three formulas involved with waves? How do you decide which one to use?
11) Are SI units important? What are the SI units for: wavelength; frequency; velocity; time?
12) Convert these to SI units: a) 500kHz, b) 35cm, c) 4.6MHz, d) 4 cm/s, e) 2½ mins.
13) Find the speed of a wave with frequency 50 kHz and wavelength 0.3 cm.
14) Find the time period of a wave of wavelength 1.5 km and speed 3×10^8 m/s.
15) A crash of thunder is heard 6 seconds after the flash of lightning. How far away is it?
16) If the sea bed is 600 m down, how long will it take to receive a sonar echo from it?
17) Sketch the patterns when plane ripples reflect at a) plane surface, b) a curved surface.
18) Sketch the reflection of curved ripples at a plane surface.
19) What is the law of reflection? Give a sketch to illustrate diffuse reflection of light.
20) Draw a neat ray diagram to show how to locate the position of the image in a plane mirror.
21) What is refraction? What causes it? How does it affect wavelength and frequency?
22) Sketch a ray of light going through a rectangular glass block, showing the angles i and r.
23) How fast does light travel in glass? Which way does it bend as it enters glass. What if i=90°?
24) What is dispersion? Sketch the diagram which illustrates it with all the labels.
25) Sketch the three diagrams to illustrate Total Internal Reflection and the Critical Angle.
26) Sketch three applications of total internal reflection which use 45° prisms, and explain them.
27) Give details of the two main uses of optical fibres. How do optical fibres work?
28) Describe analogue and digital signals. Why are digital signals better?
29) What is diffraction? Sketch the diffraction of a) water waves b) sound waves c) light.
30) What aspect of EM waves determines their differing properties?
31) Sketch the EM spectrum with all its details. What happens when EM waves are absorbed?
32) Give full details of the uses of radio waves. How do the three different types get "around"?
33) Give full details of the two main uses of microwaves, and the three main uses of infrared.
34) Give a sensible example of the use of visible light. What is its main use?
35) Detail three uses of UV light, two uses of X-rays and three uses of gamma rays.
36) What harm will UV, X-rays and gamma rays do in <u>high</u> doses? What about in <u>low</u> doses?
37) What causes seismic waves? Sketch diagrams showing the paths of both types, and explain.
38) Draw a diagram of the internal structure of the Earth, with labels.
39) How big are the various parts in relation to each other? What is the mantle made of?
40) What is the core made of? What are the three big clues that tell us about the Earth?
41) What was the old theory about the Earth's surface? What is the theory of Plate Tectonics?
42) Give details of the five bits of evidence which support the theory of Plate Tectonics.
43) What are the three different ways that tectonic plates interact at boundaries?
44) What happens when an oceanic plate collides with a continental plate? Draw a diagram.
45) What four features does this produce? Which part of the world is the classic case of this?
46) What happens when two continental plates collide? Draw diagrams.
47) What features does this produce? Which part of the world is the classic case of this?
48) What is the mid-Atlantic ridge? What happens there?
49) Which country lies on top of it? Do they get earthquakes? What *do* they get?
50) Where is the San Andreas fault? What are the tectonic plates doing along this fault line?
51) Why does it cause Earthquakes — and why did they build San Francisco right on top of it?

The Planets

You need to revise the <u>order</u> of the planets, which is made easier by using the little jollyism below:

Mercury,	Venus,	Earth,	Mars,	(Asteroids),	Jupiter,	Saturn,	Uranus,	Neptune,	Pluto
(My	Very	Energetic	Maiden	Aunt	Just	Swam	Under	North	Pier)

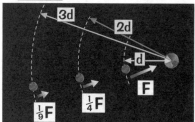

<u>Mercury</u>, <u>Venus</u>, <u>Earth</u> and <u>Mars</u> are known as the <u>inner planets</u>.
<u>Jupiter</u>, <u>Saturn</u>, <u>Uranus</u>, <u>Neptune</u> and <u>Pluto</u> are much further away and are the <u>outer planets</u>.

Planets Reflect Sunlight and Orbit in Ellipses

1) You can <u>see</u> some of the nearer planets with the <u>naked eye</u> at night, e.g. Mars and Venus.
2) They look just like <u>stars</u>, but they are of course <u>totally different</u>.
3) Stars are <u>huge</u> and <u>very far away</u> and <u>give out</u> lots of light.
   The planets are <u>smaller</u> and <u>nearer</u> and they just <u>reflect sunlight</u> falling on them.
4) The Sun, like other stars, produces <u>heat</u> from <u>nuclear fusion reactions</u> which turn <u>hydrogen</u> into <u>helium</u>.
   It gives out the <u>full spectrum</u> of <u>EM radiation</u>.
5) Planets always orbit around <u>stars</u>. In our Solar System the planets orbit the <u>Sun</u> of course.
6) These orbits are all <u>slightly elliptical</u> (elongated circles).
7) All the planets in our Solar System orbit in the <u>same plane</u> except Pluto (as shown in the pic above).
8) The <u>further</u> the planet is from the Sun, the <u>longer</u> its orbit takes (see below about Gravity).

Gravity Decreases Quickly as you get Further Away

1) With <u>very large</u> masses like <u>stars</u> and <u>planets</u>, gravity is <u>very big</u> and acts <u>a long way out</u>.
2) The <u>closer</u> you get to a star or a planet, the <u>stronger</u> the <u>force of attraction</u>.
3) To <u>counteract</u> the stronger gravity, planets nearer the Sun move <u>faster</u> and cover their orbit <u>quicker</u>.
4) <u>Comets</u> are also held in <u>orbit</u> by gravity, as are <u>moons</u> and <u>satellites</u> and <u>space stations</u>.
5) The size of the force of gravity follows the fairly famous "<u>inverse square</u>" relationship.
   The main effect of that is that the force <u>decreases very quickly</u> with increasing <u>distance</u>.
   The <u>formula</u> is $F \propto 1/d^2$, but I reckon it's <u>easier</u> just to remember the basic idea <u>in words</u>:

a) If you <u>double the distance</u> from a planet, the size of the force will <u>decrease</u> by a <u>factor of four</u> (2^2).

b) If you <u>treble the distance</u>, the <u>force</u> of gravity will <u>decrease</u> by a <u>factor of nine</u> (3^2), and so on.

c) On the other hand, if you get <u>twice as close</u> the gravity becomes <u>four times stronger</u>.

Planets in the Night Sky Seem to Move across the Constellations

1) The <u>planets</u> look just like stars except that they <u>wander</u> across the constellations over periods of <u>days or weeks</u>, often going in the <u>opposite direction</u> to the stars.
2) Their position and movement depends on <u>where</u> they are in their orbit, compared to <u>us</u>.
3) This <u>peculiar movement</u> of the planets made the <u>early astronomers</u> realise that the Earth was <u>not the centre</u> of the Universe after all, but was in fact just the <u>third rock from the Sun</u>.
   It's <u>very strong evidence</u> for the <u>Sun-centred</u> model of the Solar System.
4) Alas, the boys at the <u>Spanish Inquisition</u> were less than keen on such heresy, and poor old <u>Copernicus</u> had a pretty hard time of it for a while. In the end though, "<u>the truth will out</u>".

Learn This Page — but keep shtum to the boys in the Red Robes...

Isn't the Solar System great! All those pretty coloured planets and all that big black empty space. You can look forward to one or two easy questions on the planets — or you might get two real horrors instead. Be ready, <u>learn</u> all the <u>nitty gritty details</u> till you know it all real good.

Moons, Meteorites, Asteroids and Comets

Moons are Heavenly Bodies Which Orbit Planets

1) The Earth only has <u>one</u> moon of course, but some of the <u>other planets</u> have <u>quite a few</u>.

2) We can only <u>see</u> the moon because it <u>reflects sunlight</u>.

3) The <u>phases of the moon</u> happen depending on <u>how much</u> of the <u>illuminated side</u> of the moon we can <u>see</u>, as shown:

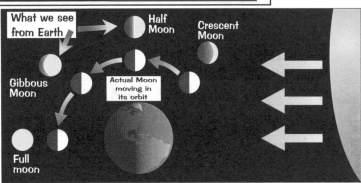

Asteroids are a Belt of Rocks Orbiting Between Mars and Jupiter

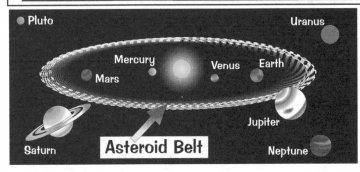

1) There are <u>several thousand</u> lumps of <u>rock</u> orbiting the Sun in a <u>belt</u> between the orbits of <u>Mars</u> and <u>Jupiter</u>.

2) They <u>vary in size</u> from about <u>1,000 km</u> diameter down to just <u>1 km</u>.

3) These <u>asteroids</u> usually <u>stay in their orbits</u> but if they <u>collide</u> and get <u>knocked out</u> of their orbits they become <u>meteors</u>...

Meteors are Lumps of Rock that Crash Down to Earth

1) Don't confuse <u>meteors</u> with <u>asteroids</u>.

2) <u>Asteroids</u> stay in a <u>nice steady orbit</u> round the Sun.

3) <u>Meteors</u> are asteroids that get <u>knocked out</u> of their nice steady orbit and then <u>collide with Earth</u>.

4) When they enter the <u>Earth's atmosphere</u> they <u>burn up</u>, and we then see them as <u>shooting stars</u>.

5) If they're <u>big enough</u>, they reach the <u>Earth's surface</u>. This is <u>rare</u>, but it's <u>serious</u> when they do.

Comets Orbit the Sun, but have very Eccentric (elongated) Orbits

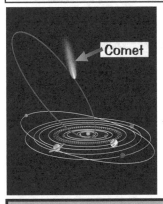

1) <u>Comets</u> only appear <u>every few years</u> because their <u>orbits</u> take them <u>very far from the Sun</u> and then <u>back in close</u>, which is when <u>we</u> see them.

2) The Sun is <u>not at the centre</u> of the orbit but <u>near one end</u> as shown.

3) Comet <u>orbits</u> can be in <u>different planes</u> from the orbits of the planets.

4) Comets are made of <u>ice</u> and <u>rock</u> and, as they approach the Sun, the <u>ice melts</u> leaving a <u>bright tail</u> of <u>debris</u> which can be <u>millions of km</u> long.

5) The comet travels <u>much faster</u> when it's <u>nearer the Sun</u> than it does when it's in the more <u>distant</u> part of its orbit.
This is because the <u>pull of gravity</u> makes it <u>speed up</u> as it gets <u>closer</u>, and then <u>slows it down</u> as it gets <u>further away</u> from the Sun.

Learn about these Lumps of Rock — and watch out for them...

Four more cosmic bits and bobs for you to know about. There's more to a Solar System than just planets you know. Make sure you learn all the details about these different lumps of rock. It's all in the syllabus, so they could ask you about any of it. Four <u>mini-essays</u> please. Now.

Satellites

Moons are sometimes called <u>natural satellites</u>.
<u>Artificial satellites</u> are sent up by humans for <u>four</u> main purposes:
1) Monitoring <u>Weather</u>.
2) <u>Communications</u>, e.g. phone and TV.
3) <u>Space research</u> such as the Hubble Telescope.
4) <u>Spying</u> on baddies.
There are <u>two different orbits</u> useful for satellites:

1) Geostationary Satellites are Used For Communications

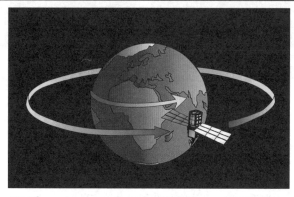

1) These can also be called <u>geosynchronous</u> satellites.
2) They are put in <u>quite a high orbit</u> over the <u>Equator</u> which takes <u>exactly 24 hours</u> to complete.
3) This means that they <u>stay above the same point</u> on the Earth's surface because the Earth <u>rotates with them</u> — hence the name Geo(*Earth*)-stationary.
4) This makes them <u>ideal</u> for <u>telephone</u> and <u>TV</u> because they're always in the <u>same place</u> and they can <u>transfer signals</u> from one side of the Earth to another in a <u>fraction of a second</u>.

5) There is room for about <u>400</u> geostationary satellites — any more and their orbits will <u>interfere</u>.

2) Low Polar Orbit Satellites are for Weather and Spying

1) In a <u>low polar orbit</u>, the satellite sweeps over <u>both poles</u> whilst the Earth <u>rotates beneath it</u>.

2) The time taken for each full orbit is just <u>a few hours</u>.

3) Each time the satellite comes round it can <u>scan</u> the next bit of the globe.

4) This allows the <u>whole surface</u> of the planet to be <u>monitored</u> each day.

5) Geostationary satellites are <u>too high</u> to take good weather or spying photos, but the satellites in <u>polar orbits</u> are <u>nice and low</u>.

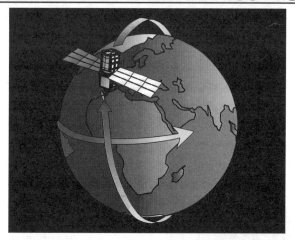

3) The Hubble Telescope has no Atmosphere in the way

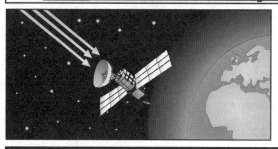

1) The <u>big advantage</u> of having telescopes on <u>satellites</u> is that they can look out into space <u>without</u> the <u>distortion</u> and <u>blurring</u> caused by the Earth's <u>atmosphere</u>.

2) This allows much <u>greater detail</u> to be seen of <u>distant stars</u> and also the <u>planets</u> in the Solar System.

Learn about Satellites — and look down on your friends...

You can actually see the low polar orbit satellites on a nice dark clear night. They look like stars except they move quite fast in a dead straight line across the sky. You're never gonna spot the geostationary ones though! <u>Learn all the details</u> about satellites, ready for seizing juicy marks.

Searching for Life on Other Planets

There's a good chance that life exists somewhere else in the Universe.
Scientists use three methods to search for anything from amoebas to little green men.

1) SETI Looks for Radio Signals from Other Planets

1) Us Earthlings are constantly beaming radio, TV and radar into space for any passing aliens to detect. There might be life out there that's as clever as we are. Or even more clever. They may have built transmitters to send out signals like ours.

2) SETI stands for "Search for Extra Terrestrial Intelligence". Scientists on the SETI project are looking for narrow bands of radio wavelengths coming to Earth from outer space. They're looking for meaningful signals in all the 'noise' (see P.43)

3) Signals on a narrow band can only come from a transmitter. The 'noise' comes from giant stars and gas clouds.

4) It takes ages to analyse all the radio waves so the SETI folk get help from the public — you can download a screen saver off the internet which analyses a chunk of radio waves.
5) SETI has been going for the last 40 years but they've not found anything. Not a sausage. ☹
6) Scientists are now looking for possible laser signals from outer space. Watch this space...

2) Robots Collect Photos and Samples

This could be a microscopic fossil of a bacteria-like organism from Mars... Then again, it could be a crystal, bits of metal or the remains of last night's curry... 500 nm

1) Scientists have sent robots in spacecrafts to Mars and Europa (one of Jupiter's moons) to look for microorganisms.
2) The robots wander round the planet, sending photographs back to Earth or collecting samples for analysis.
3) Scientists can detect living things or evidence of them, such as fossils or remains, in the samples. This "fossil" is from Mars, though no one really seems sure what it is.
4) OK, so a couple of bacteria is a bit boring but that's how we started out on Earth...

3) Chemical Changes and Reflected Light Are Big Clues

Changes Show There's Life

1) Scientists are looking for chemical changes in the atmospheres of other planets.
2) Some changes are just caused by things like volcanoes but others are a clue that there's life there.
3) The amounts of oxygen and carbon dioxide in Earth's atmosphere have changed over time — it's very different to what it'd be like if there was no life here. Plants have made oxygen levels go up but carbon dioxide levels go down.
4) They look at planet's atmospheres from Earth — no spacecraft required.

Light Gives Away What's On The Surface

A planet's reflected light (from the Sun) is different depending on whether it's bounced off rock, trees, water or whatever. It's a good way to find out what's on the surface of a planet.

Scientists haven't found anything exciting (surprise surprise) but they are using these methods to search for planets with suitable conditions for life.

I've got SETI — it's great for watching telly on...

You need to learn these three different ways that scientists are looking for life on other planets. You definitely need to learn this stuff, even if you get given more information in the exam. Cover the page and write notes about how the methods work and what they've found.

The Universe

Stars and Solar Systems form from Clouds of Dust

1) Stars form from <u>clouds of dust</u> which <u>spiral in together</u> due to <u>gravitational attraction</u>.

2) The gravity <u>compresses</u> the matter so much that <u>intense heat</u> develops and sets off <u>nuclear fusion reactions</u> and the star then begins <u>emitting light</u> and other <u>radiation</u>.

3) At the <u>same time</u> that the star is forming, <u>other lumps</u> may develop in the <u>spiralling dust clouds</u> and these eventually gather together and form <u>planets</u> which orbit <u>around the star</u>.

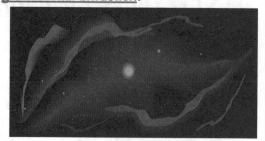

Our Sun is in The Milky Way Galaxy

1) The <u>Sun</u> is one of <u>many millions</u> of <u>stars</u> which form the <u>Milky Way Galaxy</u>.

2) The <u>distance</u> between neighbouring stars is usually <u>millions of times greater</u> than the distance between <u>planets</u> in our Solar System.

3) <u>Gravity</u> is of course the <u>force</u> which keeps the stars <u>together</u> in a <u>galaxy</u> and, like most things in the Universe, the <u>galaxies all rotate</u>, kinda like a catherine wheel only <u>much slower</u>.

4) Our Sun is out towards the <u>end</u> of one of the <u>spiral arms</u> of the Milky Way galaxy.

You are here

You are here

The Whole Universe has More Than A Billion Galaxies

1) <u>Galaxies</u> themselves are often <u>millions of times further apart</u> than the <u>stars</u> are within a galaxy.

2) So even the slowest amongst you will soon begin to realise that the Universe is <u>mostly empty space</u> and is <u>really really big</u>. Have you ever been to the NEC? Yeah? Well, it's even bigger than that.

Black Holes Don't Let Anything Escape

1) The gravity on neutron stars, white dwarfs and black dwarfs is <u>so strong</u> that it <u>crushes atoms</u>. The stuff in the stars gets <u>squashed up</u> so much that they're <u>MILLIONS OF TIMES DENSER</u> than anything on Earth.

2) If <u>enough</u> matter is left behind after a supernova explosion, it's <u>so dense</u> that <u>nothing</u> can escape the powerful gravitional field. Not even electromagnetic waves. The dead star is then called a <u>black hole</u>. Black holes <u>aren't visible</u> because any light being emitted is sucked right back in there (that's why it's called 'black', d'oh).

3) Astronomers can detect black holes in other ways — they can observe <u>X-rays</u> emitted by <u>hot gases</u> from other stars as they spiral into the black hole.

Galaxies, Milky Way — shove that down yer black hole...

More gripping facts about the Universe. Just look at those numbers: there's <u>billions</u> of stars in the Milky Way, the universe contains <u>billions</u> of galaxies, all <u>many times</u> further apart than 100,000 light years... Doesn't it just blow your socks off...

The Life Cycle of Stars

Stars go through many traumatic stages in their lives — just like teenagers.

Clouds of Dust and Gas

1) Stars initially form from clouds of DUST AND GAS.

Protostar

2) The force of gravity makes the dust particles come spiralling in together. As they do, gravitational energy is converted into heat energy and the temperature rises.

Main Sequence Star

3) When the temperature gets high enough, hydrogen nuclei undergo nuclear fusion to form helium nuclei and give out massive amounts of heat and light. A star is born. It immediately enters a long stable period where the heat created by the nuclear fusion provides an outward pressure to balance the force of gravity pulling everything inwards. In this stable period it's called a MAIN SEQUENCE STAR and it lasts about 10 billion years. (The Sun is in the middle of this stable period or to put it another way, the Earth has already had half its innings before the Sun engulfs it!)

Red Giant

4) Eventually the hydrogen begins to run out and the star then swells into a RED GIANT. It becomes red because the surface cools.

5) A small star like our Sun will then begin to cool and contract into a WHITE DWARF and then finally, as the light fades completely, it becomes a BLACK DWARF. (That's going to be really sad.)

Small stars

White Dwarf

Black Dwarf

Big stars

6) Big stars however, start to glow brightly again as they undergo more fusion and expand and contract several times forming heavier elements in various nuclear reactions. Eventually they'll explode in a SUPERNOVA.

new planetary nebula...   ...and a new solar system

Supernova

Neutron Star...

7) The exploding supernova throws the outer layers of dust and gas into space leaving a very dense core called a NEUTRON STAR. If the star is big enough this will become a BLACK HOLE.

...or Black Hole

8) The dust and gas thrown off by the supernova will form into SECOND GENERATION STARS like our Sun. The heavier elements are only made in the final stages of a big star just before the final supernova, so the presence of heavier elements in the Sun and the inner planets is clear evidence that our beautiful and wonderful world, with its warm sunsets and fresh morning dews, has all formed out of the snotty remains of a grisly old star's last dying sneeze.

9) The matter from which neutron stars and white dwarfs and black dwarfs are made is MILLIONS OF TIMES DENSER than any matter on Earth because the gravity is so strong it even crushes the atoms.

Twinkle Twinkle little star, How I wond.. — JUST LEARN IT PAL...

Erm. Just how do they know all that? As if it's not outrageous enough that they reckon to know the whole history of the Earth for the last five billion years, they also reckon to know the whole life cycle of stars, when they're all billions and billions of km away. It's just an outrage.

The Origin of the Universe

The <u>Big Bang Theory</u> of the Universe is the <u>most convincing</u> at the present time. There is also the <u>steady state theory</u> which is quite presentable but it <u>doesn't explain</u> some of the observed features too well.

Red-shift and Background Radiation need Explaining

There are <u>three important bits of evidence</u> you need to know about:

1) Light From Other Galaxies is Red-Shifted

1) When we look at <u>light from distant galaxies</u> we find that <u>all the frequencies</u> are <u>shifted</u> towards the <u>red end</u> of the spectrum.

2) In other words, the <u>frequencies</u> are all <u>slightly lower</u> than they should be. It's the same effect as a car <u>horn</u> sounding lower-pitched when the car is travelling <u>away</u> from you. The sound <u>drops in frequency</u>.

3) This is called the *DOPPLER EFFECT*.

4) <u>Measurements</u> of the red-shift suggest that <u>all the galaxies</u> are <u>moving away from us</u> very quickly — and it's the <u>same result</u> whichever direction you look in.

2) The Further Away a Galaxy is, The Greater The Red-Shift

1) <u>More distant</u> galaxies have <u>greater</u> red-shifts than nearer ones.

2) This means that more distant galaxies are <u>moving away faster</u> than nearer ones.

3) The inescapable <u>conclusion</u> appears to be that the whole Universe is <u>expanding</u>.

3) There's a Uniform Microwave Radiation From All Directions

1) This <u>low frequency radiation</u> comes from <u>all directions</u> and from <u>all parts</u> of the Universe.

2) It's known as the <u>background radiation</u> (of the Big Bang). It's nothing to do with radioactive background radiation on Earth.

3) For complicated reasons this background radiation is <u>strong evidence</u> for an <u>initial Big Bang</u>, and as the Universe <u>expands and cools</u>, so this background radiation "<u>cools</u>" and <u>drops in frequency</u>.

The Steady State Theory of the Universe — Not Popular

1) This is based on the idea that the Universe appears pretty much the <u>same everywhere</u> and <u>always has done</u>.

2) In other words the Universe has <u>always existed</u> and <u>always will</u> in the same form that it is now.

3) This theory explains the <u>apparent expansion</u> of the Universe by suggesting that <u>matter</u> is being <u>created</u> in the spaces as the Universe expands.

4) However, as yet, there's <u>no convincing explanation</u> of <u>where</u> this new matter <u>comes from</u>.

5) There isn't much support for the steady state theory, especially since the discovery of <u>background radiation</u> which fits in <u>much better</u> with the idea of a Big Bang.

6) But you <u>just never know</u>...

The Origin and Future of the Universe

The Big Bang Theory — Well Popular

1) Since all the galaxies appear to be <u>moving apart</u> very rapidly, the <u>obvious conclusion</u> is that there was an <u>initial explosion</u>: the <u>Big Bang</u>.

2) All the matter in the Universe initially occupied <u>a very small space</u> and then it <u>exploded</u> and the <u>expansion</u> is still going on.

3) The Big Bang is believed to have happened around <u>15 billion years ago</u>.

4) The age of the Universe can be <u>estimated</u> from the <u>current rate of expansion</u>.

5) These estimates are <u>not very accurate</u> because it's hard to tell how much the expansion has <u>slowed down</u> since the Big Bang.

6) The rate at which the expansion is <u>slowing down</u> is an <u>important factor</u> in deciding the <u>future</u> of the Universe.

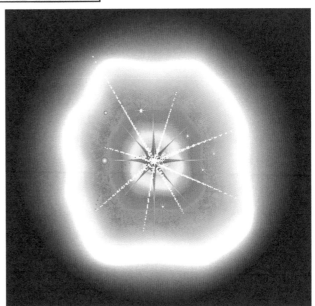

7) <u>Without gravity</u> the Universe would expand at the <u>same rate forever</u>.

8) However, the <u>attraction</u> between all the mass in the Universe tends to <u>slow</u> the expansion down.

The Future of the Universe:

It Could Expand Forever — or Collapse into The Big Crunch

1) The eventual fate of the Universe depends on <u>how fast</u> the galaxies are <u>moving apart</u> and how much <u>total mass</u> there is in it.

2) We can <u>measure</u> how fast the galaxies are <u>separating</u> quite easily, but we'd also like to know just <u>how much mass</u> there is in the Universe in order to <u>predict the future</u> of it.

3) This is proving <u>tricky</u> as most of the mass appears to be <u>invisible</u>, e.g. <u>black holes</u>, <u>big planets</u>, <u>interstellar dust</u> etc.

Anyway, depending on <u>how much mass</u> there is, there are <u>two ways</u> the Universe could go:

1) Le Crunch — But Only if there's Enough Mass

If there's <u>enough mass</u> compared to <u>how fast</u> the galaxies are currently moving, the Universe will eventually <u>stop expanding</u> and <u>begin contracting</u>. This would end in a <u>Big Crunch</u>.
The Big Crunch could be followed by another Big Bang and then <u>endless cycles</u> of <u>expansion and contraction</u>.

2) If there's Too Little Mass — then it's Le Miserable Eternity

If there's <u>too little mass</u> in the Universe to slow the expansion down, then it could <u>expand forever</u> with the Universe becoming <u>more and more spread out</u> into eternity. This seems <u>way too dismal</u> for my liking. I much prefer the idea of the Universe going <u>endlessly in cycles</u>.
But what was there <u>before</u> the Universe? Or what is there <u>outside</u> of it? It's <u>mindboggling</u>.

Time and Space — it's funny old stuff isn't it...

I think it's great that they've put all this stuff on space in the syllabus. I mean wow, something in Physics that's actually interesting. The great thing about learning a few bits and bobs about the Universe is that it can make you sound really clever when you tell people about it. "Ah well, it's all to do with the diminishing Doppler red-shift over the last 15 billion years", you can say.

Revision Summary for Section Four

The Universe is completely mindblowing in its own right. But surely the most mindblowing thing of all is the very fact that we are actually here, sitting and contemplating the truly outrageous improbability of our own existence. If your mind isn't blowing, then it hasn't sunk in yet. Think about it. 15 billion years ago there was a huge explosion, but there was no need for the whole chain of events to happen which allowed (or caused?) intelligent life to evolve and develop to the point where it became conscious of its own existence, not to mention the very disturbing unlikelihood of it all. But we have. We're here. Maaaan — is that freaky or what? The Universe could so easily have existed without conscious life ever evolving. Or come to that, the Universe needn't exist at all. Just black nothingness. So why does it exist? And why are we here?

And why do we have to do so much revision? Who knows — but stop dreaming and get on with it.

1) List the eleven parts of the Solar System starting with the Sun, and get them in the right order.
2) What do planets look like in the night sky? Which ones can be seen with the naked eye?
3) How does the Sun produce all its heat? What does the Sun give out?
4) Which is the biggest planet? Which is the smallest? Which one has an unusual orbit?
5) What is it that keeps the planets in their orbits? What shape are their orbits?
6) What is the famous "inverse square" relationship all about? Sketch a diagram to explain it.
7) What are constellations? What do planets do in the constellations?
8) Who had trouble with the boys in the red robes? Why did he have such trouble?
9) Sketch a diagram to explain the phases of the moon.
10) What and where are the asteroids? What and where are meteorites? Is there a difference?
11) What and where are comets? What are they made of? Sketch a diagram of a comet orbit.
12) What are natural and artificial satellites? What four purposes do we have for satellites?
13) Explain fully what a geostationary satellite does, and state what they're used for.
14) Explain fully what a low polar orbit satellite does, and state what they're used for.
15) What is the Hubble telescope and where is it? What's the big idea there then?
16) What does SETI stand for? Why are they looking for narrow band signals?
17) What two things do robots on planets send back? Which places have they sent robots to?
18) Describe 2 ways that scientists look for life on a planet without sending a spacecraft there.
19) Has life been found on other planets?
20) What do stars and solar systems form from? What force causes it all to happen?
21) What is the Milky Way? Sketch it and show our Sun in relation to it.
22) What is the Universe made up of? How big is it?
23) What's odd about the gravity on neutron stars, white dwarfs and black dwarfs?
24) Why would a black hole form? Why's it called 'black'? How can you spot one?
25) Describe the first stages of a star's formation. Where does the initial energy come from?
26) What process eventually starts inside the star to make it produce so much heat and light?
27) What is a "main sequence" star? How long does it last? What happens after that?
28) What are the final two stages of a small star's life?
29) What are the two final stages of a big star's life?
30) What is meant by a "second generation" star? How do we know our Sun is one?
31) What are the two main theories for the origin of the Universe? Which one is most likely?
32) What are the three important bits of evidence which need explaining by these theories?
33) Give brief details of both theories. How long ago did each suggest the Universe began?
34) What are the two possible futures for the Universe?
35) What do these possible futures depend upon?
36) How strange is the Universe? What's the most mindblowing thing ever?

Energy Transfer

Learn all The Ten Types Of Energy

You should know all of these <u>well enough</u> by now to list them <u>from memory</u>, including the examples:

1) <u>ELECTRICAL</u> ENERGY............................... — whenever a <u>current</u> flows.
2) <u>LIGHT</u> ENERGY.. — from the <u>Sun</u>, <u>light bulbs</u> etc.
3) <u>SOUND</u> ENERGY...................................... — from <u>loudspeakers</u> or anything <u>noisy</u>.
4) <u>KINETIC</u> ENERGY, or <u>MOVEMENT</u> ENERGY........ — anything that's <u>moving</u> has it.
5) <u>NUCLEAR</u> ENERGY.................................... — released only from <u>nuclear reactions</u>.
6) <u>THERMAL</u> ENERGY or <u>HEAT</u> ENERGY.............. — <u>flows</u> from <u>hot objects</u> to colder ones.
7) <u>RADIANT HEAT</u> ENERGY, or <u>INFRA RED</u> HEAT..... — given out as <u>EM radiation</u> by <u>hot objects</u>.
8) <u>GRAVITATIONAL POTENTIAL</u> ENERGY.............. — possessed by anything which can <u>fall</u>.
9) <u>ELASTIC POTENTIAL</u> ENERGY....................... — stretched <u>springs</u>, <u>elastic</u>, <u>rubber bands</u>, etc.
10) <u>CHEMICAL</u> ENERGY.................................. — possessed by <u>foods</u>, <u>fuels</u> and <u>batteries</u>.

Potential- and Chemical- are forms of Stored Energy

The <u>last three</u> above are forms of <u>stored energy</u> because the energy is not obviously <u>doing</u> anything, it's kind of <u>waiting to happen</u>, i.e. waiting to be turned into one of the <u>other</u> forms.

They Like Giving Exam Questions on Energy Transfers

These are <u>very important examples</u>. You must <u>learn them</u> till you can repeat them all <u>easily</u>.

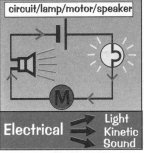

Eating food / respiration

Chemical ⇄ Heat kinetic chemical

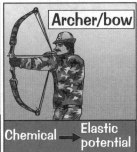

crane

Chemical → Gravitational Potential

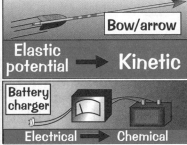

falling object

Gravitational Potential → Kinetic

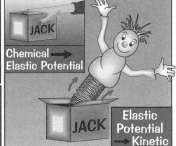

Wave Generator

Kinetic → Electrical

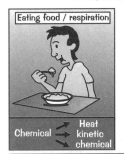

Microphone/amp/speaker

Sound → Electrical → Sound

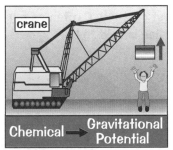

Solar panel

Light → Heat

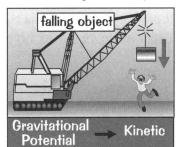

Solar cell

Light → Electrical

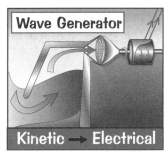

wind turbine

Kinetic → Electrical

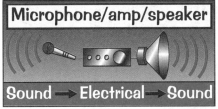

circuit/lamp/motor/speaker

Electrical ⇒ Light Kinetic Sound

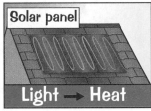

Archer/bow

Chemical → Elastic potential

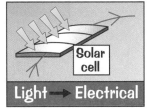

Bow/arrow

Elastic potential → Kinetic

Battery charger

Electrical → Chemical

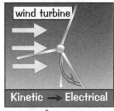

JACK

Chemical Elastic Potential

JACK

Elastic Potential → Kinetic

And <u>DON'T FORGET</u> — <u>ALL types of ENERGY</u> are measured in <u>JOULES</u>

Learn about Energy — and just keep working at it...

They're pretty keen on the different types of energy and also energy transfers. You'll definitely get an Exam question on it, and if you learn all the stuff on this page, you should have it pretty well covered I'd think. <u>Learn, cover, scribble, check, learn, cover, scribble</u>, etc. etc.

Conservation of Energy

There are Two Types of "Energy Conservation"

Try and get your head round the difference between these two.

1) "ENERGY CONSERVATION" is all about using less fossil fuels because of the damage it does and because they might run out. That's all environmental stuff, and it's fairly trivial, on a cosmic scale.

2) The "PRINCIPLE OF THE CONSERVATION OF ENERGY" on the other hand, is one of the major cornerstones of modern Physics. It's an all-pervading principle which governs the workings of the entire physical Universe. If this principle were not so, then life as we know it would simply cease to be.

3) Got it now? Good. Well don't forget.

The Principle of the Conservation of Energy can be stated thus:

ENERGY can never be *CREATED* nor *DESTROYED*
— it's only ever *CONVERTED* from one form to another.

Another important principle which you need to learn is this one:

Energy is *ONLY USEFUL* when it's *CONVERTED* from one form to another.

Most Energy Transfers Involve Some Losses, as Heat

1) Useful devices are only useful because they convert energy from one form to another.
2) In doing so, some of the useful input energy is always lost or wasted, often as heat.
3) The less energy that is wasted, the more efficient the device is said to be.

4) The energy flow diagram is pretty much the same for all devices. You must learn this basic energy flow diagram:

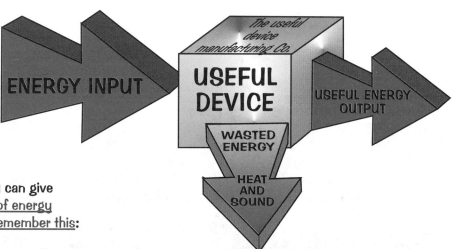

ENERGY INPUT → USEFUL DEVICE → USEFUL ENERGY OUTPUT / WASTED ENERGY → HEAT AND SOUND

For any specific example you can give more detail about the types of energy being input and output, but remember this:

_NO_ device is 100% efficient and the _WASTED ENERGY_ is always dissipated as _HEAT_ and _SOUND_.

Electric heaters are the exception to this. They're 100% efficient because all the electricity is converted to "useful" heat. What else could it become? Ultimately, all energy ends up as heat energy. If you use an electric drill, it gives out various types of energy but they all quickly end up as heat. That's an important thing to realise. So realise it — and never forget it.

Learn about energy dissipation — but keep your cool...

The thing about loss of energy is it's always the same — it always disappears as heat and sound, and even the sound ends up as heat pretty quickly. So when they ask "Why is the input energy more than the output energy?", the answer is always the same... Learn and enjoy.

Efficiency of Machines

A <u>machine</u> is a device which turns <u>one type of energy</u> into <u>another</u>.
The <u>efficiency</u> of any device is defined as:

<u>Efficiency</u> = $\dfrac{USEFUL \text{ Energy } OUTPUT}{TOTAL \text{ Energy } INPUT}$

$$\dfrac{\text{Energy out}}{\text{Efficiency} \times \text{Energy in}}$$

You can give efficiency as a <u>fraction</u>, <u>decimal</u> or <u>percentage</u>. i.e. <u>¾ or 0.75 or 75%</u>

Come on — Efficiency is Really Simple...

1) You find how much energy is <u>supplied</u> to a machine. (The Total Energy <u>INPUT</u>.)
2) You find how much <u>useful energy</u> the machine <u>delivers</u>. (The Useful Energy <u>OUTPUT</u>.)
   They either tell you this directly or they tell you how much it <u>wastes</u> as heat/sound.
3) Either way, you get those <u>two important numbers</u> and then just <u>divide</u> the <u>smaller one</u> by the <u>bigger one</u> to get a value for <u>efficiency</u> somewhere between <u>0 and 1</u> (or <u>0 and 100%</u>). Easy.
4) The other way they might ask it is to tell you the <u>efficiency</u> and the <u>input energy</u> and ask for the <u>energy output</u>. The best way to tackle that is to <u>learn</u> this <u>other version</u> of the formula:

<u>USEFUL ENERGY OUTPUT</u> = <u>Efficiency</u> × TOTAL Energy INPUT

Five Important Examples on Efficiency for you to Learn

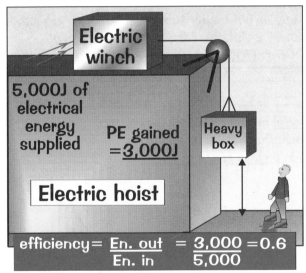

Electric winch

5,000J of electrical energy supplied

PE gained = <u>3,000J</u>

Heavy box

Electric hoist

efficiency = $\dfrac{\text{En. out}}{\text{En. in}} = \dfrac{3,000}{5,000} = 0.6$

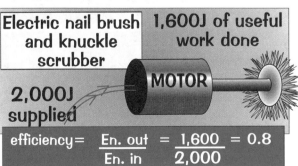

Electric nail brush and knuckle scrubber

1,600J of useful work done

MOTOR

2,000J supplied

efficiency = $\dfrac{\text{En. out}}{\text{En. in}} = \dfrac{1,600}{2,000} = 0.8$

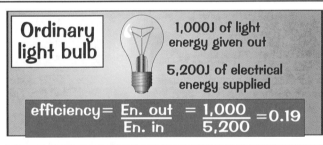

Ordinary light bulb

1,000J of light energy given out

5,200J of electrical energy supplied

efficiency = $\dfrac{\text{En. out}}{\text{En. in}} = \dfrac{1,000}{5,200} = 0.19$

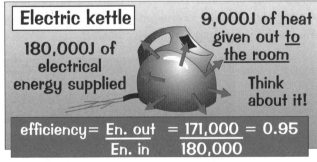

Electric kettle

180,000J of electrical energy supplied

9,000J of heat given out <u>to the room</u>

Think about it!

efficiency = $\dfrac{\text{En. out}}{\text{En. in}} = \dfrac{171,000}{180,000} = 0.95$

Low energy light bulb

1,000J of light energy given out

1,200J of electrical energy supplied

efficiency = $\dfrac{\text{En. out}}{\text{En. in}} = \dfrac{1,000}{1,200} = 0.83$

Learn about energy transfer — but do it efficiently...

Efficiency is another hideously simple concept. It's a big funny-looking word I grant you, but that doesn't mean it's tricky. Let's face it, efficiency's a blummin' doddle — divide E_{out} by E_{in} and there it is, done. Geesh. <u>Learn the page</u>, then <u>cover it up</u> and <u>scribble down</u> what you know.

Work Done, Energy and Power

When a force moves an object, energy is transferred and work is done.

That statement sounds far more complicated than it needs to. Try this:

1) Whenever something moves, something else is providing some sort of "effort" to move it.
2) The thing putting the effort in needs a supply of energy (like fuel or food or electricity etc.).
3) It then does "work" by moving the object — and one way or another it transfers the energy it receives (as fuel) into other forms.
4) Whether this energy is transferred "usefully" (e.g. by lifting a load) or is "wasted" (e.g. lost as friction), you can still say that "work is done". Just like Batman and Bruce Wayne, "work done" and "energy transferred" are indeed "one and the same". (And they're both in Joules)

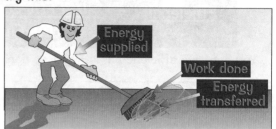

It's Just Another Trivial Formula:

Work Done = Force × Distance

Whether the force is friction or weight or tension in a rope, it's always the same. To find how much energy has been transferred (in Joules), you just multiply the force in N by the distance moved in m. Easy as that. I'll show you...

EXAMPLE: Some hooligan kids drag an old tractor tyre 5m over rough ground. They pull with a total force of 340N. Find the energy transferred.
ANSWER: Wd = F×d = 340 × 5 = 1700J.   Phew — easy peasy isn't it?

Power is the "Rate of Doing Work" — i.e. how much per second

Power is not the same thing as force, nor energy. A powerful machine is not necessarily one which can exert a strong force (though it usually ends up that way). A powerful machine is one which transfers a lot of energy in a short space of time. This is the very easy formula for power:

Power = Work done / Time taken

EXAMPLE: A motor transfers 4.8kJ of useful energy in 2 minutes. Find its power output.
ANSWER: P = Wd / t = 4,800/120 = 40W (or 40 J/s)
(Note that the kJ had to be turned into J, and the minutes into seconds.)

Power is Measured in Watts (or J/s)

The proper unit of power is the Watt. One Watt = 1 Joule of energy transferred per second. Power means "how much energy per second", so Watts are the same as "Joules per second" (J/s). Don't ever say "watts per second" — it's nonsense.

Revise work done — what else...

"Energy transferred" and "work done" are the same thing. I wonder how many times I need to say that before you'll remember. Power is "work done divided by time taken". I wonder how many times you've got to see that before you realise you're supposed to learn it as well...

Kinetic Energy and Potential Energy

Kinetic Energy is Energy of Movement

Anything which is <u>moving</u> has <u>kinetic energy</u>.
There's a slightly <u>tricky formula</u> for it, so you have to concentrate a little bit
<u>harder</u> for this one. But hey, that's life — it can be real tough sometimes:

$$\text{Kinetic Energy} = \frac{1}{2} \times \text{mass} \times \text{velocity}^2$$

K.E.
$$\frac{\text{K.E.}}{\frac{1}{2} \times m \times v^2}$$

<u>EXAMPLE</u>: A car of mass 2450kg is travelling at 38m/s.
Calculate its kinetic energy.

<u>ANSWER</u>: It's pretty easy. You just plug the numbers into the formula but watch the "V²"!
$KE = \frac{1}{2}mv^2 = \frac{1}{2} \times 2450 \times 38^2 = \underline{1\ 768\ 900J}$ (<u>Joules</u> because it's <u>energy</u>)
(When the car stops suddenly, all this energy is dissipated as heat in the brakes — it's a lot of heat.)

Remember, the <u>kinetic energy</u> of something depends both on <u>mass</u> and <u>speed</u>.
The <u>more it weighs</u> and the <u>faster it's going</u>, the <u>bigger</u> its kinetic energy will be.

small mass, not fast
low kinetic energy

big fast
lorries Ltd

big mass, real fast
high kinetic energy

Potential Energy is Energy Due to Height

$$\text{Potential Energy} = \text{mass} \times g \times \text{height}$$

P.E.
$$\frac{\text{P.E.}}{m \times g \times h}$$

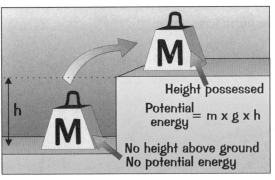

Height possessed
Potential energy $= m \times g \times h$

No height above ground
No potential energy

The proper name for this kind of "<u>Potential Energy</u>" is
<u>Gravitational Potential Energy</u>, (as opposed to "<u>elastic</u>
potential energy" or "<u>chemical</u> potential energy").
The proper name for g is "<u>gravitational field strength</u>".
On <u>Earth</u>, g is approximately <u>10m/s²</u>.

<u>EXAMPLE</u>: A sheep of mass 47kg is slowly raised through 6.3m.
Find the gain in potential energy.

<u>ANSWER</u>: It's even easier than before.
You just plug the numbers into the formula:
$PE = mgh = 47 \times 10 \times 6.3 = \underline{2961\ J}$
(<u>Joules</u> again because it's <u>energy</u> again.)

What do you call a sheep with no eyes and no legs?
Dunno?
A Cloud!

Strictly speaking it's the <u>change</u> in potential energy we're dealing with, so the formula can
sometimes be written as: "<u>Change</u> in Potential Energy = mass × g × <u>change</u> in height".
But that's a minor detail really, because it all works out just the same anyway.

Kinetic Energy — just get a move on and learn it, OK...

Phew! A couple of tricky formulae for you here. I mean gosh they've got more than three
letters in them. Still, at least they fit into formula triangles, so you may still have some small
chance of getting them right. Come on, I'm joking. Formulae are always a <u>doddle</u> aren't they?

K.E. and P.E. — Two Important Examples

1) Calculating Your Power Output

Both cases use the same formula:

$$POWER = \frac{ENERGY\ TRANSFERRED}{TIME\ TAKEN} \quad or \quad P = \frac{E}{t}$$

a) The Timed Run Upstairs:

In this case the "energy transferred" is simply the potential energy you gain (= mgh).
Hence   Power = mgh/t

Power output
= En. transferred/time
= mgh/t
= (62×10×12)÷14
= <u>531W</u>

b) The Timed Acceleration:

This time the energy transferred is the kinetic energy you gain (= ½mv²).
Hence   Power = ½mv²/t

Power output
= En. transferred/time
= ½mv²/t
= (½×62×8²)÷4
= <u>496W</u>

2) Calculating the Speed of Falling Objects

When something falls, its potential energy is converted into kinetic energy (Principle of Conservation of Energy — see P. 64). Hence the further it falls, the faster it goes. In practice, some of the PE will be dissipated as heat due to air resistance, but in Exam questions they'll likely say you can ignore air resistance, in which case you'll just need to remember this simple and really quite obvious formula:

> ### Kinetic energy gained = Potential Energy lost

EXAMPLE: A mouldy tomato of mass 140g is dropped from a height of 1.7m. Calculate its speed as it hits the floor.

ANSWER: There are four key steps to this method — and you've gotta learn them:

Step 1) Find the PE lost: = mgh = 0.14×10×1.7 = <u>2.38J</u>   This must also be the KE gained.

Step 2) Equate the number of Joules of KE gained to the KE formula with v in, " ½mv²":
$$2.38 = \tfrac{1}{2}mv^2$$

Step 3) Stick the numbers in: $2.38 = \tfrac{1}{2} \times 0.14 \times v^2$ or $2.38 = 0.07 \times v^2$
$$2.38 \div 0.07 = v^2 \quad so \quad v^2 = 34$$

Step 4) Square root: $v = \sqrt{34}$ = <u>5.83 m/s</u>

Easy peasy? Not really no, but if you practise learning the four steps you'll find it's not too bad.

The Bouncing Ball — Same % Drop in Energy and Height

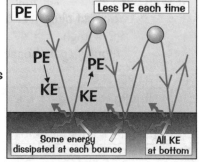

1) A bouncing ball is constantly swapping its energy between PE and KE, just as in the above example. As it falls it converts PE into KE. After the bounce, it rises again and converts its KE back into PE.

2) However, each time it bounces it will lose some energy in the bounce. This means it'll leave the surface a bit slower than it hits it, which means with less KE, so it won't reach the same height as the previous bounce.

3) The relation between total energy and height reached is really simple: If the ball loses say 10% of its energy each bounce, then the height reached will also be 10% lower each time. It's as simple as that.

Revise Falling Objects — just don't lose your grip...

This is it. This is the zenith of GCSE Physics. This is the nearest it gets to real Physics (A-level). Look at that terrifying square root sign for a start — and a four step method. It's scary stuff.

You only need to learn this page if you're doing the AQA syllabus.

69

Heat Transfer

There are three distinct methods of heat transfer: conduction, convection *and* radiation.
To answer Exam questions, you must use those three key words in just the right places,
And that means you need to know exactly what they are, and all the differences between them.

Heat Energy Causes Molecules to Move Faster

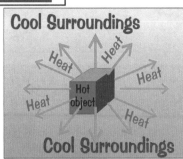

Cool Surroundings

Cool Surroundings

1) Heat energy causes gas and liquid molecules to move around faster, and causes particles in solids to vibrate more rapidly.
2) When particles move faster it shows up as a rise in temperature.
3) This extra kinetic energy in the particles tends to get dissipated to the surroundings.
4) In other words, the heat energy tends to flow away from a hotter object to its cooler surroundings.
But then you knew that already. I would hope.

> If there's a difference in temperature between two places then **HEAT WILL FLOW** between them.

Conduction, Convection and Radiation Compared

These differences are really important — make sure you learn them:
1) Conduction occurs mainly in solids.
2) Convection occurs mainly in gases and liquids.
3) Gases and liquids are very poor conductors — convection is usually the dominant process. Where convection can't occur, the heat transfer by conduction is very slow indeed as the diagram of the immersion heater shows. This is a classic example, so it's a pretty good plan to learn it.
4) Radiation travels through anything see-through including a vacuum.
5) Heat Radiation is given out by anything which is warm or hot.
6) The amount of heat radiation which is absorbed or emitted depends on the colour and texture of the surface.
But don't forget, convection and conduction are totally unaffected by surface colour or texture. A shiny white surface conducts just as well as a matt black one.

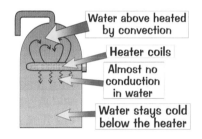

Water above heated by convection

Heater coils

Almost no conduction in water

Water stays cold below the heater

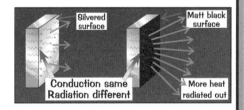

Silvered surface

Matt black surface

Conduction same
Radiation different

More heat radiated out

Convection Heaters and "Radiators" — Watch out!

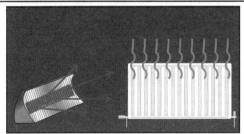

1) A "radiator" strictly should be something that glows red and gives most heat out as radiation, like a coal fire or an electric bar radiator.

2) Central heating "radiators" have the wrong name really, because they're not like that at all. They give most heat out as convection currents of warm rising air. This is what a "convection heater" does.

Learn the facts on heat transfer — but don't get a sweat on...

Phew, no more numbers and formulas, now we're back to good old straightforward factual learning again. Much less confusing — but no less of a challenge, it has to be said. You've really got to make a fair old effort to get those three key processes of heat transfer all sorted out in your head so that you know exactly what they are and when they occur. Learn and grin.

Section Five — Energy

You only need to learn this page if you're doing the <u>AQA</u> syllabus.

Conduction and Convection of Heat

Conduction of Heat — Occurs Mainly in Solids

<u>*CONDUCTION OF HEAT*</u> is the process where <u>*VIBRATING PARTICLES*</u> pass on their <u>*EXTRA KINETIC ENERGY*</u> to <u>*NEIGHBOURING PARTICLES*</u>.

This process continues <u>throughout the solid</u> and gradually the <u>extra kinetic energy</u> (or <u>heat</u>) is passed all the way through the solid, causing a <u>rise in temperature</u> at the other side.

All Metals Are Good Conductors due to their Free Electrons

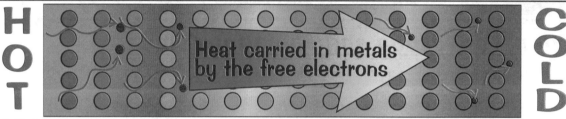

1) Metals "<u>conduct</u>" so well because the electrons are <u>free to move</u> inside the metal.
2) At the <u>hot end</u>, the electrons move <u>faster</u> and <u>diffuse more quickly</u> through the metal.
3) So the electrons <u>carry their energy</u> quite a <u>long way</u> before <u>giving it up</u> in a <u>collision</u>.
4) This is obviously a much <u>faster way</u> of <u>transferring the energy</u> through the metal than slowly passing it between <u>jostling neighbouring atoms</u>. This is why <u>heat travels so fast</u> through <u>metals</u>.

Metals always FEEL hotter or colder because they conduct so well

You'll notice if a <u>spade</u> is left out in the <u>sunshine</u> that the <u>metal</u> part will always <u>feel</u> much <u>hotter</u> than the <u>wooden</u> handle. <u>But it isn't hotter</u> — it just <u>conducts</u> the heat <u>into your hand</u> much quicker than the wood, so your hand <u>heats up</u> much quicker.
In <u>cold weather</u>, the <u>metal bits</u> of a spade, or anything else, always <u>feel colder</u> because they <u>take the heat away</u> from your hand quicker. But they're <u>not colder</u>... Remember that.

Convection of Heat — Liquids and Gases Only

<u>Gases and liquids</u> are usually free to <u>slosh about</u> — and that allows them to transfer heat by <u>convection</u>, which is a <u>much more effective process</u> than conduction.
Convection simply <u>can't happen in solids</u> because the particles <u>can't move</u>.

<u>Convection</u> occurs when the more energetic particles <u>move</u> from the <u>hotter region</u> to the <u>cooler region</u> — <u>and take their heat energy with them</u>

When the <u>more energetic</u> (i.e. <u>hotter</u>) particles get somewhere <u>cooler</u> they then <u>transfer their energy</u> by the usual process of <u>collisions</u> which warm up the surroundings.

Good conductors are always metals? — what about Simon Rattle...

Oi! Watch out! It's another pair of Physics words that look so much alike that half of you think they're the same word. Look: CONVECTION. See, it's different from CONDUCTION. Tricky that one isn't it. Just like reflection and refraction. Not just a different word though — convection is a <u>totally different process</u> too. Make sure you learn exactly <u>why</u> it isn't like conduction.

Heat Radiation

<u>Heat radiation</u> can also be called <u>infra-red radiation</u>, and it consists purely of electromagnetic waves of a certain frequency. It's just below visible light in the <u>electromagnetic spectrum</u>.

Heat Radiation Can Travel Through A Vacuum

<u>Heat radiation</u> is <u>different</u> from the <u>other two methods</u> of heat transfer in quite a few ways:

1) It travels in <u>straight lines</u> at the <u>speed of light</u>.

2) It travels through a <u>vacuum</u>. This is the <u>only way</u> that heat can reach us from the <u>Sun</u>.

3) It can be very effectively <u>reflected away</u> <u>again</u> by a <u>silver surface</u>.

4) It only travels through <u>transparent</u> <u>media</u>, like <u>air</u>, <u>glass</u> and <u>water</u>.

5) Its behaviour is <u>strongly dependent</u> on <u>surface colour and texture</u>. This definitely <u>isn't</u> so for conduction and convection.

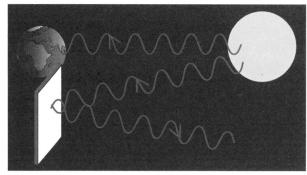

Emission and Absorption of Heat Radiation

1) <u>All objects</u> are <u>continually</u> emitting and absorbing <u>heat radiation</u>.

2) The <u>hotter</u> they are, the <u>more</u> heat radiation they <u>emit</u>.

3) <u>Cooler ones</u> around them will <u>absorb</u> this heat radiation. You can <u>feel</u> this <u>heat radiation</u> if you stand near something <u>hot</u> like a fire.

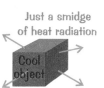

Just a smidge of heat radiation

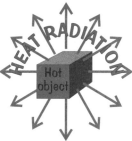

It Depends An Awful Lot on Surface Colour and Texture

1) <u>Dark matt</u> surfaces <u>absorb</u> heat radiation falling on them much more <u>strongly</u> than <u>bright glossy</u> surfaces, such as <u>gloss white</u> or <u>silver</u>. They <u>also emit</u> heat radiation <u>much more</u> too.

2) <u>Silvered</u> surfaces <u>reflect</u> nearly all heat radiation falling on them.

3) In the lab, there are several fairly dull experiments to demonstrate the <u>effects of surface</u> on <u>emission</u> and <u>absorption</u> of <u>heat radiation</u>. Here are two of the most gripping:

Leslie's Cube

The <u>matt black</u> side <u>emits most heat</u> so its that thermometer which gets <u>hottest</u>.

The <u>matt black</u> surface <u>absorbs most heat</u> so its wax <u>melts</u> first and the ball bearing <u>drops</u>.

The Melting Wax Trick

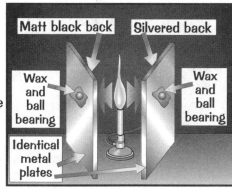

Revise Heat Radiation — absorb as much as you can anyway...

The main thing to learn here is that heat radiation is strongly affected by the colour and texture of surfaces. Don't forget that the other two types of heat transfer, conduction and convection, are not affected by surface colour and texture <u>at all</u>. Heat radiation is totally different from conduction and convection. <u>Learn</u> all the details on this page, then <u>cover it up</u> and <u>scribble</u>.

Applications of Heat Transfer

Good Conductors and Good Insulators

1) All <u>metals</u> are good <u>conductors</u> e.g. iron, brass, aluminium, copper, gold, silver etc.

2) All <u>non-metals</u> are good <u>insulators</u>.

3) Gases and liquids are truly <u>abysmal conductors</u> (but are great <u>convectors</u> don't forget).

4) The <u>best insulators</u> are ones which <u>trap pockets of air</u>. If the air <u>can't move</u>, it <u>can't</u> transfer heat by <u>convection</u> and so the heat has to <u>conduct</u> very slowly through the <u>pockets of air</u>, as well as the material in between. This really slows it down <u>bigstyle</u>.
This is how <u>clothes</u> and <u>blankets</u> and <u>loft insulation</u> and <u>cavity wall insulation</u> and <u>polystyrene cups</u> and <u>pretty woollen mittens</u> and <u>little furry animals</u> and <u>fluffy yellow ducklings</u> work.

Insulation should also take account of Heat Radiation

1) <u>Silvered finishes</u> are highly effective <u>insulation</u> against heat transfer by <u>radiation</u>.

2) This can work <u>both ways</u>, either keeping heat radiation <u>out</u> or keeping heat <u>in</u>.

KEEPING HEAT RADIATION OUT:	*KEEPING HEAT IN:*
Spacesuits	Shiny metal kettles
Cooking foil on the turkey	Survival blankets
Thermos flasks	Thermos flasks (again)

3) <u>Matt black</u> is rarely used for its thermal properties of <u>absorbing</u> and <u>emitting</u> heat radiation.

4) It's only <u>useful</u> where you want to <u>get rid of heat</u>, e.g. the <u>cooling fins</u> or <u>radiator</u> on an engine.

The Thermos Flask — The Ultimate in Insulation

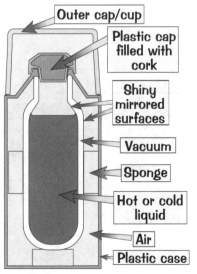

Outer cap/cup

Plastic cap filled with cork

Shiny mirrored surfaces

Vacuum

Sponge

Hot or cold liquid

Air

Plastic case

1) The glass bottle is <u>double-walled</u> with a <u>thin vacuum</u> between the two walls. This stops <u>all conduction and convection</u> through the <u>sides</u>.

2) The walls either side of the vacuum are <u>silvered</u> to keep heat loss by <u>radiation</u> to a <u>minimum</u>.

3) The bottle is supported using <u>insulating foam</u>. This minimises heat <u>conduction</u> to or from the <u>outer</u> glass bottle.

4) The <u>stopper</u> is made of <u>plastic</u> and filled with <u>cork or foam</u> to reduce any <u>heat conduction</u> through it.

In <u>Exam questions</u> you must <u>always</u> say which form of heat transfer is involved at any point, either <u>conduction</u>, <u>convection</u> or <u>radiation</u>.
"The vacuum stops heat getting out" will get you <u>no marks at all</u>.

Heat Transfer and Insulation — keep taking it all in...

There's a lot more to insulation than you first realise. That's because there are <u>three ways</u> that heat can be transferred, and so effective heat insulation has to deal with <u>all three</u>, of course. The venerable Thermos Flask is the classic example of all-in-one full-blown insulation. <u>Learn it</u>.

Keeping Buildings Warm

Loft Insulation
Initial Cost: £200
Annual Saving: £50
Payback time: 4 years

Hot Water Tank Jacket
Initial Cost: £10
Annual Saving: £15
Payback time: 1 year

Thermostatic Controls
Initial Cost: £100
Annual Saving: £20
Payback time: 5 years

Double Glazing
Initial Cost: £3,000
Annual Saving: £60
Payback time: 50 years

Cavity Wall Insulation
Initial Cost: £500
Annual Saving: £70
Payback time: 7 years

Draught-proofing
Initial Cost: £50
Annual Saving: £50
Payback time: 1 year

Effectiveness and Cost-effectiveness are not the same...

1) The figures above are all in the right "ball park", but of course it'll vary from house to house.

2) The cheaper methods of insulation tend to be a lot more cost-effective than the pricier ones.

3) The ones that save the most money each year could be considered the most "effective". i.e. cavity wall insulation. How cost-effective it is depends on what time-scale you're looking at.

4) If you subtract the annual saving from the initial cost repeatedly then eventually the one with the biggest annual saving must always come out as the winner, if you think about it.

5) But you might sell the house (or die) before that happens. If instead you look at it over say, a five year period then the cheap and cheerful draught-proofing wins. Who's to say?

6) But double glazing is always by far the least cost-effective, which is kinda comical, considering.

Know Which Types of Heat Transfer are Involved:

1) CAVITY WALL INSULATION — foam squirted into the gap between the bricks reduces convection and radiation across the gap.

2) LOFT INSULATION — a thick layer of fibreglass wool laid out across the whole loft floor reduces conduction and radiation into the roof space from the ceiling.

3) DRAUGHT PROOFING — strips of foam and plastic around doors and windows stop draughts of cold air blowing in, i.e. they reduce heat loss due to convection.

4) DOUBLE GLAZING — two layers of glass with an air gap reduce conduction and radiation.

5) THERMOSTATIC RADIATOR VALVES — these simply prevent the house being over-warmed.

6) HOT WATER TANK JACKET — lagging such as fibreglass wool reduces conduction and radiation from the hot water tank.

7) THICK CURTAINS — big bits of cloth you pull across the window to stop people looking in at you, but also to reduce heat loss by conduction and radiation.

They don't seem to have these problems in Spain...

Remember, the most effective insulation measure is the one which keeps the most heat in, (biggest annual saving). If your house had no roof, then a roof would be the most effective measure, would it not... But cost-effectiveness depends very much on the time-scale involved.

Energy Resources

There are <u>twelve</u> different types of <u>energy resource</u>.
They fit into <u>two broad types</u>: <u>renewable</u> and <u>non-renewable</u>.

Non-renewable Energy Resources Will Run Out One Day

The <u>non-renewables</u> are the <u>three FOSSIL FUELS</u> and <u>NUCLEAR</u>:

1) <u>Coal</u>

2) <u>Oil</u>

3) <u>Natural gas</u>

4) <u>Nuclear fuels</u> (<u>uranium</u> and <u>plutonium</u>)

a) They will <u>all run out</u> one day.
b) They all do <u>damage</u> to the environment.
c) But they provide <u>most of our energy</u>.

Renewable Energy Resources Will Never Run Out

The <u>renewables</u> are:

1) <u>Wind</u>

2) <u>Waves</u>

3) <u>Tides</u>

4) <u>Hydroelectric</u>

5) <u>Solar</u>

6) <u>Geothermal</u>

7) <u>Food</u>

8) <u>Biomass (wood)</u>

a) These will <u>never run out</u>.
b) They <u>do not damage the environment</u> (except visually).
c) The trouble is they <u>don't provide much energy</u> and many of them are <u>unreliable</u> because they depend on the <u>weather</u>.

The Sun is the Ultimate Source for Nine of The Energy Resources

(The exceptions are tides, nuclear and geothermal — see below)
You need to know the <u>energy transfer chains</u> for all nine of them starting from the <u>Sun</u>.
There are however only five basic <u>energy chains</u>:

1) <u>Sun</u> ➡ <u>light energy</u> ➡ <u>plants</u> ➡ <u>photosynthesis</u> ➡ BIOMASS (wood) or FOOD.

2) <u>Sun</u> ➡ <u>light energy</u> ➡ <u>photosynthesis</u> ➡ <u>dead plants/animals</u> ➡ FOSSIL FUELS.

3) <u>Sun</u> ➡ <u>heats atmosphere</u> ➡ <u>creates WINDS</u> ➡ <u>and therefore WAVES too</u>.

4) <u>Sun</u> ➡ <u>heating sea water</u> ➡ <u>clouds</u> ➡ <u>rain</u> ➡ HYDROELECTRICITY.

5) <u>Sun</u> ➡ <u>light energy</u> ➡ SOLAR POWER.

The Sun Generates Its Energy by Nuclear Fusion Reactions

1) <u>Hydrogen nuclei</u> fuse together to form <u>helium nuclei</u>.
2) This <u>energy</u> is given off as <u>EM waves</u> which reach the Earth as <u>light and heat radiation</u>.

Nuclear, Geothermal and Tidal Energy Do NOT Originate in the Sun

1) <u>Nuclear power</u> comes from the energy <u>locked up</u> in the <u>nuclei of atoms</u>.
2) <u>Nuclear decay</u> also creates heat <u>inside the Earth</u> for <u>geothermal energy</u>, though this happens <u>much slower</u> than in a nuclear reactor.
3) <u>Tides</u> are caused by the <u>gravitational attraction</u> of the <u>Moon</u> and <u>Sun</u>.

Stop fuelling around and learn this stuff properly...

There's a lot of details here on sources of energy — an awful lot of details. Trouble is, in the Exam they could test you on any of them, so I guess you just gotta learn 'em. Most of this page seems to be made up of lists, which is quite a novelty. There you go then, life isn't all bad.

Power Stations Using Non-Renewables

Most of the electricity we use is generated from the four NON-RENEWABLE sources of energy (coal, oil, gas and nuclear) in big power stations, which are all pretty much the same apart from the boiler. Learn the basic features of the typical power station shown here and also the nuclear reactor.

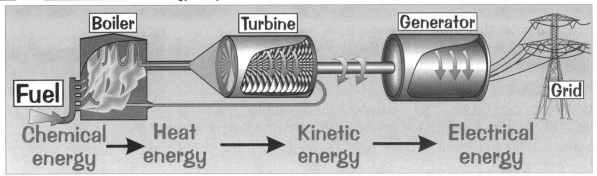

Boiler — Turbine — Generator — Grid — Fuel

Chemical energy → Heat energy → Kinetic energy → Electrical energy

Nuclear Reactors are Just Fancy Boilers

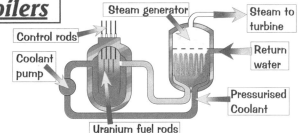

1) A nuclear power station is mostly the same as the one shown above, where heat is produced in a boiler to make steam to drive turbines etc. The difference is in the boiler, as shown here:
2) They take the longest time of all the non-renewables to start up. Natural gas takes the shortest time.

Steam generator, Control rods, Coolant pump, Uranium fuel rods, Steam to turbine, Return water, Pressurised Coolant

Environmental Problems With The Use Of Non-Renewables

1) All three fossil fuels, (coal, oil and gas) release CO_2. For the same amount of energy produced, coal releases the most CO_2, followed by oil then gas. All this CO_2 adds to the Greenhouse Effect, causing global warming. There's no feasible way to stop it being released either. Ho hum.
2) Burning coal and oil releases sulphur dioxide which causes acid rain. This is reduced by taking the sulphur out before it's burned or cleaning up the emissions.
3) Coal mining makes a mess of the landscape, especially "open-cast mining".
4) Oil spillages cause serious environmental problems. We try to avoid it, but it'll always happen.
5) Nuclear power is clean but the nuclear waste is very dangerous and difficult to dispose of.
6) Nuclear fuel (i.e. uranium) is cheap but the overall cost of nuclear power is high due to the cost of the power plant and final de-commissioning.
7) Nuclear power always carries the risk of a major catastrophe like the Chernobyl disaster.

The Non-Renewables Need to be Conserved

1) When the fossil fuels eventually run out we will have to use other forms of energy.
2) More importantly however, fossil fuels are also a very useful source of chemicals, (especially crude oil) which will be hard to replace when they are all gone.
3) To stop the fossil fuels running out so quickly there are two things we can do:

1) Use Less Energy by Being More Efficient With it:
(i) Better insulation of buildings,
(ii) Turning lights and other things off when not needed,
(iii) Making everyone drive spiddly little cars with puny little engines.

2) Use More Of The Renewable Sources Of Energy
as detailed on the following pages.

Learn about the non-renewables — before it's too late...
Make sure you realise that we generate most of our electricity from the four non-renewables, and that the power stations are all pretty much the same, as exemplified by the above diagram. Also make sure you know all the problems about them and why we should use less of them.

Wind Power and Hydroelectric Power

Wind Power — Lots of Little Wind Turbines

1) This involves putting <u>lots of windmills</u> (wind turbines) up in <u>exposed places</u> like on <u>moors</u> or round <u>coasts</u>.

2) Each wind turbine has its own <u>generator</u> inside it so the electricity is generated <u>directly</u> from the <u>wind</u> turning the <u>blades</u>, which <u>turn the generator</u>.

3) There's <u>no pollution</u>.

4) But they do <u>spoil the view</u>. You need about <u>5000 wind turbines</u> to replace <u>one coal-fired power station</u> and 5000 of them cover <u>a lot</u> of ground — that wouldn't look very nice at all.

5) There's also the problem of <u>no power when the wind stops</u>, and it's <u>impossible</u> to <u>increase supply</u> when there's <u>extra demand</u>.

6) The <u>initial costs are quite high</u>, but there are <u>no fuel costs</u> and <u>minimal running costs</u>.

Hydroelectricity and Pumped Storage Systems

1) <u>Hydroelectric power</u> usually requires the <u>flooding</u> of a <u>valley</u> by building a <u>big dam</u>.

2) <u>Rainwater</u> is caught and allowed out <u>through turbines</u>. There is <u>no pollution</u>.

3) There is quite a <u>big impact</u> on the <u>environment</u> due to the flooding of the valley and possible <u>loss of habitat</u> for some species. The reservoirs can also look very <u>unsightly</u> when they <u>dry up</u>. Location in <u>remote valleys</u> (in <u>Scotland</u> and <u>Wales</u>) tends to avoid these problems on the whole.

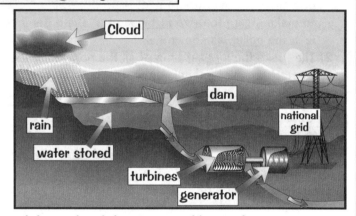

4) A <u>big advantage</u> is <u>immediate response</u> to increased demand and there's no problem with <u>reliability</u> except in times of <u>drought</u> — but remember this is *Great Britain* we're talking about.

5) <u>Initial costs are high</u> but there's <u>no fuel</u> and <u>minimal running costs</u>.

Pumped Storage Gives Extra Supply Just When it's Needed

1) Most large power stations have <u>huge boilers</u> which have to be kept running <u>all night</u> even though demand is <u>very low</u>. This means there's a <u>surplus</u> of electricity at night.

2) It's surprisingly <u>difficult</u> to find a way of <u>storing</u> this spare energy for <u>later use</u>.

3) <u>Pumped storage</u> is one of the <u>best solutions</u> to the problem.

4) In pumped storage, 'spare' <u>night-time electricity</u> is used to pump water up to a <u>higher reservoir</u>.

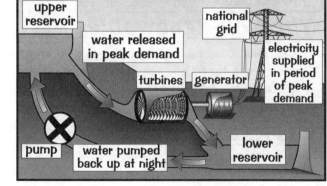

5) This can then be <u>released quickly</u> during periods of <u>peak demand</u> such as at <u>tea time</u> each evening, to supplement the <u>steady delivery</u> from the big power stations.

6) Remember, <u>pumped storage</u> uses the same <u>idea</u> as Hydroelectric Power but it <u>isn't</u> a way of <u>generating</u> power — but simply a way of <u>storing energy</u> which has <u>already</u> been generated.

Learn about Wind Power — it can blow your mind...

Lots of important details here on these nice green squeaky clean sources of energy — pity they make such a mess of the landscape. Three nice green squeaky clean <u>mini-essays</u> please.

Wave Power and Tidal Power

Don't confuse <u>wave power</u> with <u>tidal power</u>. They are <u>completely different</u>.

Wave Power — Lots of little Wave Converters

1) You need lots of small <u>wave generators</u> located <u>around the coast</u>.

2) As waves come in to the shore they provide an <u>up and down motion</u> which can be used to drive a <u>generator</u>.

3) There is <u>no pollution</u>. The main problems are <u>spoiling the view</u> and being a <u>hazard to boats</u>.

4) They are <u>fairly unreliable</u>, since waves tend to die out when the <u>wind drops</u>.

5) <u>Initial costs are high</u> but there's <u>no fuel</u> and <u>minimal running costs</u>. Wave power is never likely to provide energy on a <u>large scale</u> but it can be <u>very useful</u> on <u>small islands</u>.

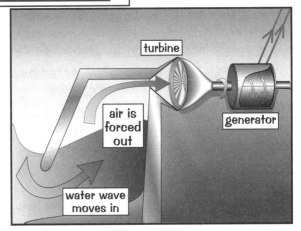

Tidal Barrages — Using The Sun and Moon's Gravity

1) <u>Tidal barrages</u> are <u>big dams</u> built across <u>river estuaries</u> with <u>turbines</u> in them.

2) As the <u>tide comes in</u> it fills up the estuary to a height of <u>several metres</u>. This water can then be allowed out <u>through turbines</u> at a controlled speed. It also drives the turbines on the way in.

3) There is <u>no pollution</u>. The source of the energy is the gravity of the Sun and the moon.

4) The main problems are <u>preventing free access by boats</u>, <u>spoiling the view</u> and <u>altering the habitat</u> of the wildlife eg: wading birds, sea creatures and beasties who live in the sand.

5) Tides are <u>pretty reliable</u> in the sense that they happen <u>twice a day without fail</u>, and always to the <u>predicted height</u>. The only drawback is that the <u>height</u> of the tide is <u>variable</u> so lower (neap) tides will provide <u>significantly less energy</u> than the bigger "<u>spring</u>" tides. But tidal barrages are <u>excellent</u> for <u>storing energy</u> ready for periods of <u>peak demand</u>.

6) <u>Initial costs are moderately high</u> but there's <u>no fuel</u> and <u>minimal running costs</u>. Even though it can only be used in a <u>few</u> of the <u>most suitable estuaries</u> tidal power has the potential for generating a <u>significant amount</u> of energy.

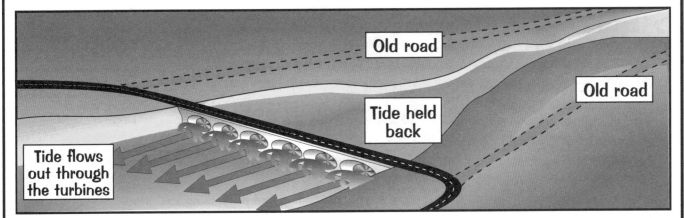

Learn about Wave Power — and bid your cares goodbye...

I do hope you appreciate the big big differences between tidal power and wave power. They both involve salty sea water, sure — but there the similarities end. Lots of jolly details then, just waiting to be absorbed into your cavernous intra-cranial void. Smile and enjoy. And <u>learn</u>.

Geothermal and Wood Burning

Geothermal Energy — Heat From Underground

1) This is <u>only possible</u> in <u>certain places</u> where <u>hot rocks</u> lie quite near to the <u>surface</u>. The source of much of the heat is the <u>slow decay</u> of various <u>radioactive elements</u> including <u>uranium</u> deep inside the Earth.

2) <u>Water is pumped</u> in pipes down to <u>hot rocks</u> and <u>returns as steam</u> to drive a <u>generator</u>.

3) This is actually <u>brilliant free energy</u> with no real environmental problems.

4) The <u>main drawback</u> is the <u>cost of drilling</u> down <u>several km</u> to the hot rocks.

5) Unfortunately there are <u>very few places</u> where this seems to be an <u>economic option</u> (for now).

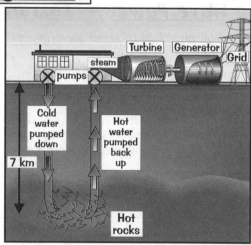

Wood Burning — Environmentally OK

1) This can be done <u>commercially</u> on a <u>large scale</u>.

2) It involves the cultivation of <u>fast-growing trees</u> which are then <u>harvested</u>, <u>chopped up</u> and <u>burned</u> in a power station <u>furnace</u> to produce <u>electricity</u>.

3) Unlike <u>fossil fuels</u>, wood burning does <u>not</u> cause a problem with the <u>Greenhouse Effect</u> because any CO_2 released in the burning of the wood was <u>removed</u> when they <u>grew in the first place</u>, and because the trees are grown <u>as quickly as they are burnt</u> they will <u>never run out</u>.
This does **NOT apply** to the burning of <u>rainforests</u> where the trees take <u>much longer</u> to grow.

4) The <u>main drawback</u> is the <u>use of land</u> for <u>growing trees</u>, but if these woods can be made into <u>recreational areas</u> then that may be a <u>positive benefit</u> and certainly the woodlands should look quite <u>attractive</u>, as opposed to 5000 wind turbines covering miles and miles of countryside.

5) As a method of electricity generation, wood burning may seem mighty <u>old-fashioned</u>, but if enough trees are grown this is a <u>reliable and plentiful source of energy</u>, with fewer environmental drawbacks than many other energy resources.

6) Initial costs <u>aren't too high</u>, but there's some cost in <u>harvesting and processing</u> the wood.

Wood Burning to solve the energy crisis? — barking mad...

I must say, I reckon on geothermal energy as being the big source of power for the next millennium or two. All you have to do is drill down 10 or 20km and you're sorted — limitless free energy. Anyway, two more squeaky clean <u>mini-essays</u> just crying out to be <u>scribbled</u>. Enjoy.

Solar Energy and Comparison

Solar Energy — Solar Cells, Solar Panels and Solar Furnaces

LEARN the three different ways that solar energy can be harnessed:

1) SOLAR CELLS generate electric currents directly from sunlight. They are expensive initially. Solar cells are the best source of energy for calculators and watches which don't use much electricity. Remote places like Antarctica and satellites don't have a choice — they have to use solar power.

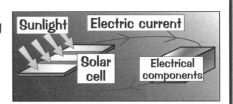

2) SOLAR PANELS are much less sophisticated. They simply contain water pipes under a black surface. Heat radiation from the Sun is absorbed by the black surface to heat the water in the pipes.

3) A SOLAR FURNACE is a large array of curved mirrors which are all focused onto one spot to produce very high temperatures so water can be turned to steam to drive a turbine.

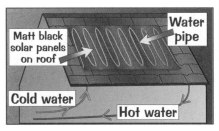

In all cases there is no pollution. In sunny countries solar power is a very reliable source of energy — but only in the daytime. Solar power will still provide some energy even in cloudy countries like Britain. Initial costs are high but after that the energy is free and running costs almost nil (apart from the solar furnaces which are more complicated).

Comparison of Renewables and Non-Renewables

1) They're quite likely to give you an Exam question asking you to "evaluate" or "discuss" the relative merits of generating power by renewable and non-renewable resources.
2) The way to get the marks is to simply write down the pros and cons of each method.
3) Full details are given on the last few pages. However there are some clear generalisations you should definitely learn to help you answer such questions. Make sure you can list these easily from memory:

Non-Renewable Resources (Coal, Oil, Gas and Nuclear):

ADVANTAGES:

1) Very high output.
2) Reliable output, entirely independent of the weather.
3) Don't take up much land or spoil too much landscape.

DISADVANTAGES:

1) Very polluting.
2) Mining or drilling, then transportation of fuels damages the environment.
3) They're running out quickly.

Renewable Resources (Wind, Waves, Solar etc.):

ADVANTAGES:

1) No pollution.
2) They will never run out.
3) Don't damage the environment (except visually).
4) No fuel costs, although the initial costs are high.

DISADVANTAGES:

1) Require large areas of land or water.
2) They don't always deliver when needed — if the weather isn't right, for example.
3) Don't provide much energy.

Solar Cells are like Fried Eggs — always best sunny side up...

Watch out for it — there are three different ways of using solar power directly. Learn all three. And make sure you learn all that summary comparing renewables and non-renewables. Phew.

Revision Summary for Section Five

There are three distinct parts to Section Five. First there's power, work done, efficiency etc. which involve a lot of formulas and calculations. Then there's heat transfer, which is trickier to fully get the grip of than most people realise, and finally there's the stuff on generating power, which is basically easy but there are lots of drivelly details to learn. Make sure you realise the different approach needed for all three bits and focus your planet-sized brain accordingly.

Blue questions are for AQA bods <u>only</u>.

1) List the ten different types of energy, and give twelve different examples of energy transfers.
2) Write down the Principle of the Conservation of Energy. When is energy actually <u>useful</u>?
3) Sketch the basic energy flow diagram for a typical "useful device".
4) What forms does the wasted energy always take?
5) What's the formula for efficiency? What are the three numerical forms suitable for efficiency?
6) Is efficiency really easy or really complicated? Give three worked examples on efficiency.
7) What's the connection between "work done" and "energy transferred"?
8) What's the formula for work done? A crazy dog drags a big branch 12m over the next-door neighbour's front lawn, pulling with a force of 535N. How much energy was transferred?
9) What's the formula for power? What are the units of power?
10) An electric motor uses 540kJ of electrical energy in 4½ minutes. What is its power consumption? If it has an efficiency of 85%, what's its power output?
11) Write down the formulas for KE and PE. Find the KE of a 78kg sheep moving at 23m/s.
12) Calculate the power output of a 78kg sheep which runs 20m up a staircase in 16.5 seconds.
13) Calculate the speed of a 78kg sheep as it hits the floor after falling from a height of 20m.
14) If the sheep bounces back up to a height of 18m calculate the % loss of KE at the bounce.
15) What causes heat to flow from one place to another? What do molecules do as they heat up?
16) Explain briefly the difference between conduction, convection and radiation.
17) Give a strict definition of conduction of heat and say which materials are good conductors.
18) Give a strict definition of convection. Give two examples of natural and forced convection.
19) List five properties of heat radiation. Which kind of objects emit and absorb heat radiation?
20) Which surfaces absorb heat radiation best? Which surfaces emit it best?
21) Describe two experiments to demonstrate the effect of different surfaces on radiant heat.
22) Describe insulation measures which reduce   a) conduction   b) convection   c) radiation.
23) Draw a fully labelled diagram of a Thermos Flask, and explain exactly what each bit is for.
24) List the seven main ways of insulating houses and say which are the most <u>effective</u> and which are the most <u>cost-effective</u> measures. How do you decide on cost-effectiveness?
25) List the four non-renewable sources of energy and say why they are non-renewable.
26) List the eight kinds of renewable energy.
27) Draw five energy chains which start with the Sun as the source of energy.
28) Nine out of the twelve energy resources originate in the Sun — which are they?
29) Which three energy resources do <u>not</u> originate in the Sun?
30) Which kind of resources do we get most of our energy from? Sketch a typical power station.
31) List seven environmental hazards with non-renewables and four ways that we can use less.
32) Give full details of how we can use wind power, including the advantages and disadvantages.
33) Give full details of how a hydroelectric scheme works. What's pumped storage all about?
34) Sketch a wave generator and explain the pros and cons of this as a source of energy.
35) Explain how tidal power can be harnessed. What are the pros and cons of this idea?
36) Explain where geothermal energy comes from. Describe how we can make use of it.
37) Explain the principles of wood-burning for generating electricity. Give the pros and cons.
38) Write down where solar cells are used. What are the disadvantages of solar power?
39) List the advantages and disadvantages of using renewable or non-renewable sources of energy. What does it mean when a question says "Discuss..."?

Atomic Structure and Isotopes

See the Chemistry Book for a few more details on this.

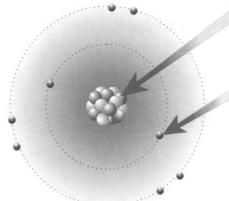

The <u>nucleus</u> contains <u>protons</u> and <u>neutrons</u>.
Most of the <u>mass</u> of the atom is contained in the <u>nucleus</u>, but it takes up <u>virtually no space</u> — it's <u>tiny</u>.

The <u>electrons</u> fly around the <u>outside</u>.
They're <u>negatively charged</u> and really really <u>small</u>.
They <u>occupy a lot of space</u> and this gives the atom its <u>overall size</u>, even though it's <u>mostly empty space</u>.

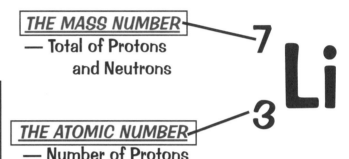

THE MASS NUMBER
— Total of Protons
and Neutrons

$_3^7Li$

THE ATOMIC NUMBER
— Number of Protons

Make sure you <u>learn this table</u>:

PARTICLE	MASS	CHARGE
Proton	1	+1
Neutron	1	0
Electron	$1/2000$	-1

Isotopes are Different Forms of The Same Element

1) <u>Isotopes</u> are atoms with the <u>same</u> number of <u>protons</u> but a <u>different</u> number of <u>neutrons</u>.
2) Hence they have the <u>same atomic number</u>, but <u>different mass numbers</u>.
3) <u>Carbon-12</u> and <u>Carbon-14</u> are good examples:

4) <u>Most elements</u> have different isotopes but there's usually only one or two <u>stable</u> ones.
5) The other isotopes tend to be <u>radioactive</u>, which means they <u>decay</u> into <u>other elements</u> and <u>give out radiation</u>. This is where all <u>radioactivity</u> comes from — <u>unstable radioactive isotopes</u> undergoing <u>nuclear decay</u> and spitting out <u>high energy particles</u>.

$_6^{12}C$ $_6^{14}C$

two extra neutrons

Rutherford's Scattering and The Demise of the Plum Pudding

1) In 1804 <u>John Dalton</u> said matter was made up of <u>tiny solid spheres</u> which he called <u>atoms</u>.
2) Later they discovered <u>electrons</u> could be <u>removed</u> from atoms. They then saw atoms as <u>spheres of positive charge</u> with tiny negative electrons <u>stuck in it</u> like plums in a <u>plum pudding</u>.

3) Then <u>Ernest Rutherford</u> and his merry men tried firing <u>alpha particles</u> at a <u>thin gold foil</u>. Most of them just went <u>straight through</u>, but the odd one came <u>straight back</u> at them, which was frankly a bit of a <u>shocker</u> for Ernie and his pals.
Being pretty clued up guys though, they realised this meant that <u>most of the mass</u> of the atom was concentrated at the <u>centre</u> in a <u>tiny nucleus</u>, with a <u>positive charge</u>.
This means that most of an atom is just made up of <u>empty space</u>, which is also a bit of a <u>shocker</u> when you think about it.

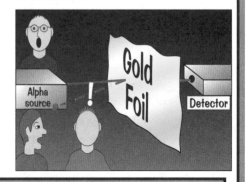

Plum Pudding Theory — by 1911 they'd had their fill of it...

Yeah, that's right — atoms are mostly empty space. When you think about it, those electrons are amazing little jokers really. They have almost no mass, no size, and a tiny little -ve charge. In the end it's only their frantic whizzing about that makes atoms what they are. It's outrageous.

The Three Types of Radiation

Don't get <u>mixed up</u> between <u>nuclear radiation</u> which is <u>dangerous</u> — and <u>electromagnetic</u> <u>radiation</u> which <u>generally isn't</u>. Gamma radiation is included in both, of course.

Nuclear Radiation: Alpha, Beta and Gamma (α, β and γ)

You need to remember <u>three things</u> about <u>each type of radiation</u>:

1) What they <u>actually are</u>.
2) How well they <u>penetrate</u> materials.
3) How strongly they <u>ionise</u> that material (i.e. bash into atoms and <u>knock electrons off</u>).
   There's a pattern: The <u>further</u> the radiation can <u>penetrate</u> before hitting an atom and getting stopped, the <u>less damage</u> it will do along the way and so the <u>less ionising</u> it is.

Alpha Particles are Helium Nuclei ^4_2He

1) They are relatively <u>big</u> and <u>heavy</u> and <u>slow moving</u>.
2) They therefore <u>don't penetrate</u> into materials but are <u>stopped quickly</u>.
3) Because of their size they are <u>strongly ionising</u>, which just means they <u>bash into a lot of atoms</u> and <u>knock electrons off</u> them before they slow down, which creates lots of ions — hence the term "<u>ionising</u>".

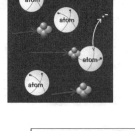

Beta Particles are Electrons $^{\ 0}_{-1}\text{e}$

1) These are <u>in between alpha and gamma</u> in terms of their <u>properties</u>.
2) They move <u>quite fast</u> and they are <u>quite small</u> (they're electrons).
3) They <u>penetrate moderately</u> before colliding and are <u>moderately ionising</u> too.
4) For every β–particle emitted, a <u>neutron</u> turns to a <u>proton</u> in the nucleus.

Gamma Rays are Very Short Wavelength EM Waves

1) They are the <u>opposite of alpha particles</u> in a way.
2) They <u>penetrate a long way</u> into materials without being stopped.
3) This means they are <u>weakly ionising</u> because they tend to <u>pass through</u> rather than colliding with atoms. Eventually they <u>hit something</u> and do <u>damage</u>.

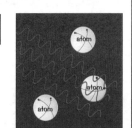

Remember What Blocks the Three Types of Radiation...

They really like this for Exam questions, so <u>make sure you know</u> what it takes to <u>block each of the three</u>:

<u>Alpha particles</u> are blocked by <u>paper</u>.
<u>Beta particles</u> are blocked by thin <u>aluminium</u>.
<u>Gamma rays</u> are blocked by <u>thick lead</u>.
Of course anything <u>equivalent</u> will also block them, e.g. <u>skin</u> will stop <u>alpha</u>, but <u>not</u> the others; a thin sheet of <u>any metal</u> will stop <u>beta</u>; and <u>very thick</u> <u>concrete</u> will stop <u>gamma</u> just like lead does.

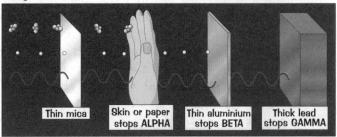

Thin mica | Skin or paper stops ALPHA | Thin aluminium stops BETA | Thick lead stops GAMMA

Learn the three types of radiation — it's easy as abc...

Alpha, beta and gamma. You do realise those are just the first three letters of the Greek alphabet don't you: α, β, γ — just like a, b, c. They might sound like complex names to you but they were just easy labels at the time. Anyway, <u>learn all the facts</u> about them — and <u>scribble</u>.

Background Radiation

Radioactivity is a Totally Random Process

Unstable nuclei will decay and in the process give out radiation. This process is entirely random. This means that if you have 1000 unstable nuclei, you can't say when any one of them is going to decay, and neither can you do anything at all to make a decay happen. Each nucleus will just decay quite spontaneously in its own good time. It's completely unaffected by physical conditions like temperature or by any sort of chemical bonding etc.

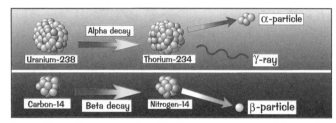

When the nucleus does decay it will spit out one or more of the three types of radiation, alpha, beta or gamma, and in the process the nucleus will often change into a new element.

As well as this natural radioactive decay, stable nuclei can be made unstable by firing neutrons at them. When stray neutrons hit a stable nucleus they will usually be absorbed into it and this generally turns it into an unstable isotope of the same element. Stray neutrons occur for example when uranium nuclei undergo fission and split in two, as shown:

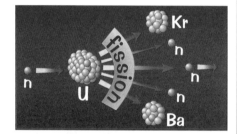

Background Radiation Comes From Many Sources

Natural background radiation comes from:

1) Radioactivity of naturally occurring unstable isotopes which are all around us — in the air, in food, in building materials and in the rocks under our feet.

2) Radiation from space, which is known as cosmic rays. These come mostly from the Sun.

3) Radiation due to human activity. i.e. fallout from nuclear explosions or dumped nuclear waste. But this represents a tiny proportion of the total background radiation.

The RELATIVE PROPORTIONS of background radiation:

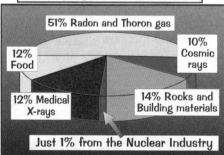

51% Radon and Thoron gas
10% Cosmic rays
12% Food
12% Medical X-rays
14% Rocks and Building materials
Just 1% from the Nuclear Industry

The Level of Background Radiation Changes Depending on Where You Are

1) At high altitudes (e.g. in jet planes) it increases because of more exposure to cosmic rays.

2) Underground in mines, etc. it increases because of the rocks all around.

3) Certain underground rocks can cause higher levels at the surface, especially if they release radioactive radon gas, which tends to get trapped inside people's houses. This varies widely across the UK depending on the rock type, as shown:

Millom

Coloured bits indicate more radiation from rocks

Background Radiation — it's no good burying your head in the sand...

Yip, it's funny old stuff is radiation, that's for sure. It is quite mysterious, I guess, but just like anything else, the more you learn about it, the less of a mystery it becomes. This page is positively bristling with simple straightforward facts about radiation. Three tiny little mini-essays practised two or three times and all this knowledge will be yours — forever. Enjoy. ☺

Uses of Radioactive Materials

This is a <u>nice easy bit</u> of <u>straightforward learning</u>. Below are the <u>seven main uses</u> for radioactive isotopes. Make sure you <u>learn all the details</u>. In particular, make sure you know why each application uses a <u>particular radio-isotope</u> according to its <u>half-life</u> and the <u>type of radiation</u> it gives out.

1) *Tracers in Medicine — always Short Half-life γ-emitters*

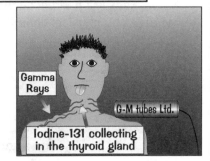

Gamma Rays

G-M tubes Ltd.

Iodine-131 collecting in the thyroid gland

1) Certain <u>radioactive isotopes</u> can be <u>injected</u> into people (or they can just <u>swallow</u> them) and their progress <u>around the body</u> can be followed using an external <u>detector</u>. A computer converts the reading to a <u>TV display</u> showing where the <u>strongest reading</u> is coming from.

2) A well known example is the use of <u>Iodine-131</u> which is absorbed by the <u>thyroid gland</u>, just like normal Iodine-127, but it gives out <u>radiation</u> which can be <u>detected</u> to indicate whether or not the thyroid gland is <u>taking in the iodine</u> as it should.

3) <u>All isotopes</u> which are taken <u>into the body</u> must be <u>GAMMA or BETA</u> (never alpha), so that the radiation <u>passes out of the body</u> and they should only last <u>a few hours</u>, so that the radioactivity inside the patient <u>quickly disappears</u>. (i.e. they should have a <u>short half-life</u>.)

2) *Tracers in Industry — For Finding Leaks*

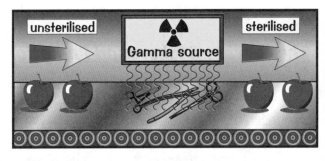

G-M tubes Ltd.

This is much the same technique as the medical tracers.
1) Radio-isotopes can be used to <u>detect leaks in pipes</u>.
2) You just <u>squirt it in</u>, and then go along the <u>outside</u> of the pipe with a <u>detector</u> to find areas of <u>extra high</u> radioactivity, which indicates the stuff is <u>leaking out</u>. This is really useful for <u>concealed</u> or <u>underground</u> pipes, to save you <u>digging up half the road</u> trying to find the leak.
3) The isotope used <u>must</u> be a <u>gamma emitter</u>, so that the radiation can be <u>detected</u> even through <u>metal or earth</u> which may be <u>surrounding</u> the pipe. Alpha and beta rays wouldn't be much use because they are <u>easily blocked</u> by any surrounding material.
4) It should also have a <u>short half-life</u> so as not to cause a <u>hazard</u> if it collects somewhere.

3) *Sterilisation of Food and Surgical Instruments Using γ-Rays*

1) <u>Food</u> can be exposed to a <u>high dose</u> of <u>gamma rays</u> which will <u>kill</u> all <u>microbes</u> thus keeping the food <u>fresh for longer</u>.

2) <u>Medical instruments</u> can be <u>sterilised</u> in just the same way, rather than <u>boiling them</u>.

3) The great <u>advantage</u> of <u>irradiation</u> over boiling is that it doesn't involve <u>high temperatures</u> so things like <u>fresh apples</u> or <u>plastic instruments</u> can be totally <u>sterilised</u> without <u>damaging</u> them.

unsterilised

sterilised

Gamma source

4) The food is <u>not</u> radioactive afterwards, so it's <u>perfectly safe</u> to eat.

5) The isotope used for this needs to be a <u>very strong</u> emitter of <u>gamma rays</u> with a <u>reasonably long half-life</u> (at least several months) so that it doesn't need <u>replacing</u> too often.

4) *Radiotherapy — the Treatment of Cancer Using γ-Rays*

1) Since high doses of gamma rays will <u>kill all living cells</u>, they can be used to <u>treat cancers</u>.
2) The gamma rays have to be <u>directed carefully</u> and at just the right <u>dosage</u> so as to kill the <u>cancer cells</u> without damaging too many <u>normal cells</u>.
3) However, a <u>fair bit of damage</u> is <u>inevitably</u> done to <u>normal cells</u> which makes the patient feel <u>very ill</u>. But if the cancer is <u>successfully killed off</u> in the end, then it's worth it.

Uses of Radioactive Materials

5) Thickness Control in Industry and Manufacturing

This is a classic application and is pretty popular in Exams. It's really very simple.

1) You have a radioactive source and you direct it through the stuff being made, usually a continuous sheet of paper or cardboard or metal etc.

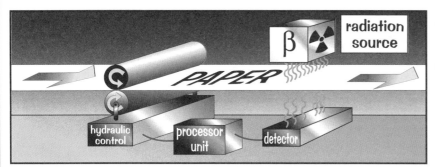

2) The detector is on the other side and is connected to a control unit.

3) When the amount of radiation detected goes down, it means the stuff is coming out too thick and so the control unit pinches the rollers up a bit to make it thinner again.

4) If the reading goes up, it means it's too thin, so the control unit opens the rollers out a bit. It's all clever stuff, but the most important thing, as usual, is the choice of isotope.

5) Firstly, it must have a long half-life (several years at least!), otherwise the strength would gradually decline and the control unit would keep pinching up the rollers trying to compensate.

6) Secondly, the source must be a beta source for paper and cardboard, or a gamma source for metal sheets. This is because the stuff being made must partly block the radiation.
If it all goes through, (or none of it does), then the reading won't change at all as the thickness changes. Alpha particles are no use for this since they would all be stopped.

6) Radioactive Dating of Rocks and Archaeological Specimens

1) The discovery of radioactivity and the idea of half-life gave scientists their first opportunity to accurately work out the age of rocks and fossils and archaeological specimens.

2) By measuring the amount of a radioactive isotope left in a sample, and knowing it's half-life, you can work out how long the thing has been around. (See P. 88)

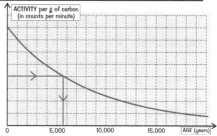

3) Igneous rocks contain radioactive uranium which has a ridiculously long half-life. It eventually decays to becomes stable isotopes of lead so the big clue to a rock sample's age is the relative proportions of uranium and lead isotopes.

4) Igneous rock also contains radioisotope potassium–40. Its decay produces stable argon gas and sometimes this gets trapped in the rock. Then it's the same process again — finding the relative proportions of potassium–40 and argon to work out the age.

7) Generating Power from Nuclear Fuel (Uranium)

1) Radioactive decay always gives out energy in the form of heat.

2) The radioactive decay inside the Earth is responsible for much of the heat down there.

3) By purifying uranium, we can set up a chain reaction where each decay causes another one. In this way we can increase the rate of reaction to generate lots of heat and then use it to produce electricity. This is what a nuclear power station does (See P. 75).

Will any of that be in your Exam? — isotope so...

First learn the seven headings till you can write them down from memory. Then start learning all the details that go with each one of them. As usual, the best way to check what you know is to do a mini-essay for each section. Then check back and see what details you missed. Nice.

Detection Of Radiation

The Geiger-Müller Tube and Counter

1) This is the most <u>familiar type</u> of <u>radiation detector</u>. You see them on **TV** documentaries going <u>click-click-clickety-click</u>, whilst the grim-faced reporter delivers a sombre message of impending doom and the terrible state of the planet.

2) This is also the type used for <u>experiments in the lab</u>, as the counter allows you to record the number of <u>counts per minute</u>.

3) When <u>alpha</u>, <u>beta</u> or <u>gamma</u> radiation enters the <u>G-M tube</u>, it <u>ionises</u> the gas inside and triggers an <u>electrical discharge</u> (a spark) which makes a <u>clicking sound</u> and also sends a <u>small signal</u> to the electronic <u>counter</u>. It's so simple even I could have thought of it... but born too late. Sigh.

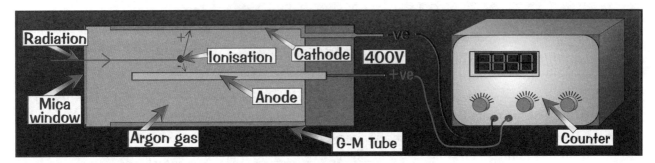

Background Count must always be Subtracted... (See P.89)

If you want to find the <u>count rate</u> from a <u>specific source</u>, you must always measure the <u>background count</u> first, (i.e. take the reading with <u>no source</u> present) and then <u>subtract</u> that value from <u>each reading</u> taken using the source. This is <u>especially important</u> if you are plotting the values on a <u>graph</u> to find the <u>half-life</u>.

Radioactivity is Measured in Becquerels, Bq

The <u>unit</u> used for measuring <u>radioactivity</u> is the <u>Becquerel</u> (Bq). <u>One Becquerel</u> is <u>one nucleus decaying per second</u>. So a count rate of <u>60 counts per minute (60 CPM)</u> would represent <u>1 Bq</u>.

In fact it's a bit tricky to measure exactly how strong a radioactive source is because the reading you get on your G-M tube/counter depends very much on how close you are to the source and how big the front window is on your G-M tube. A reading in Becquerels really only gives you a sort of vague relative measure of how much radioactivity there is around. A bigger G-M tube or moving closer to the source would give a much bigger reading in counts per second (Bq). Anyway, as long as you know that <u>one Becquerel</u> means <u>one nucleus decaying per second</u> (on average), then you'll be OK in the Exam.

Photographic Film Also Detects Radiation

1) Radiation was first <u>discovered by accident</u> when <u>Henri Becquerel</u> left some <u>uranium</u> on some <u>photographic plates</u> which became "<u>fogged</u>" by it.

2) These days <u>photographic film</u> is a useful way of detecting radiation.

3) Workers in the <u>nuclear industry</u> or those using <u>X-ray equipment</u> such as <u>dentists</u> and <u>radiographers</u> wear <u>little badges</u> which have a bit of <u>photographic film</u> in them.

4) The film is checked <u>every now and then</u> to see if it's got fogged <u>too quickly</u>, which would mean the person was getting <u>too much exposure</u> to radiation.

You can't see, hear, smell or taste it — just like truth...

Make sure you remember those two ways of measuring radiation: G-M tube and photographic film, and remember what a Becquerel is. This page is ideal for the good old mini-essay method I reckon, just to make sure you've taken all the important points on board. <u>Learn and scribble</u>.

Radiation Hazards and Safety

Radiation Harms Living Cells

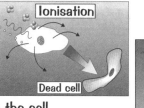

1) <u>Alpha</u>, <u>beta</u> and <u>gamma</u> radiation will cheerfully <u>enter living cells</u> and <u>collide with molecules</u>.

2) These collisions cause <u>ionisation</u>, which <u>damages or destroys</u> the <u>molecules</u>.

3) <u>Lower doses</u> tend to cause <u>minor damage</u> without <u>killing</u> the cell.

4) This can give rise to <u>mutant cells</u> which <u>divide uncontrollably</u>. This is <u>cancer</u>.

5) <u>Higher doses</u> tend to <u>kill cells completely</u>, which causes <u>radiation sickness</u> if a lot of body cells <u>all get blatted at once</u>.

6) The <u>extent</u> of the harmful effects depends on <u>two things</u>:

    a) <u>How much exposure</u> you have to the radiation.

    b) The <u>energy and penetration</u> of the radiation emitted, since <u>some types</u> are <u>more hazardous</u> than others, of course.

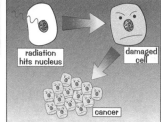

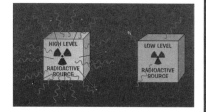

Outside The Body, β– and γ–Sources are the Most Dangerous

This is because <u>beta and gamma</u> can get <u>inside</u> to the delicate <u>organs</u>, whereas alpha is much less dangerous because it <u>can't penetrate the skin</u>.

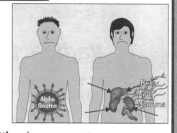

Inside The Body, an α–Source is the Most Dangerous

Inside the body alpha-sources do all their damage in a <u>very localised area</u>. Beta and gamma sources on the other hand are <u>less dangerous</u> inside the body because they mostly <u>pass straight out</u> without doing much damage.

α, β and γ are Ionising Radiation

Ionisation is when an atom either <u>loses</u> or <u>gains</u> an <u>electron</u>. Simple as that — just don't forget it.

You Need to Learn About These Safety Precautions

If you don't <u>already know</u> that radioactive materials need to be handled <u>carefully</u> then you must be some sort of <u>idiot</u>. In the Exam they might ask you to <u>list some specific precautions</u> that should be taken when <u>handling radioactive materials</u>. If you want those <u>easy marks</u> you'd better learn all these:

In the School Laboratory:

1) <u>Never</u> allow <u>skin contact</u> with a source. Always handle with <u>tongs</u>.

2) Keep the source at <u>arm's length</u> to keep it <u>as far</u> from the body <u>as possible</u>.

3) Keep the source <u>pointing away</u> from the body and <u>avoid looking directly at it</u>.

4) <u>Always</u> keep the source in a <u>lead box</u> and put it back in <u>as soon</u> as the experiment is <u>over</u>.

Extra Precautions for Industrial Nuclear Workers:

1) Wearing <u>full protective suits</u> to prevent <u>tiny radioactive particles</u> from being <u>inhaled</u> or lodging <u>on the skin</u> or <u>under fingernails</u> etc.

2) Use of <u>lead-lined suits</u> and <u>lead/concrete barriers</u> and <u>thick lead screens</u> to prevent exposure to γ-rays from highly contaminated areas. (α and β are stopped <u>much more easily</u>.)

3) Use of <u>remote controlled robot arms</u> in highly radioactive areas.

Radiation Sickness — well yes, it does all get a bit tedious...

Quite a few picky details here. It's easy to kid yourself that you don't really need to know all this stuff. Well take it from me, you <u>do</u> need to know it all and there's only one sure–fire way to find out whether you do or not. Three <u>mini-essays</u> please, with all the picky details in. Enjoy.

Nuclear Equations and Half-life

Nuclear Equations — Not Half as Bad as They Sound

Nuclear equation are OK I think. In the end it's just a case of making sure the <u>mass numbers</u> and <u>atomic numbers balance up on both sides</u>, that's all. The trickiest bit is <u>remembering</u> the <u>mass- and atomic-numbers</u> for α, β and γ particles, and <u>neutrons</u> too. Make sure you can do all of these <u>easily</u>:

1) ALPHA EMISSION:
An α-particle is simply a <u>helium nucleus</u>, mass 4 and charge of +2: $^{4}_{2}He$

A typical <u>alpha-emission</u>: $^{226}_{88}Ra \rightarrow \, ^{222}_{86}Rn + \, ^{4}_{2}He$

2) BETA EMISSION:
A β-particle is simply an <u>electron</u>, with no mass and a charge of -1: $^{0}_{-1}e$

A typical <u>beta-emission</u>: $^{14}_{6}C \rightarrow \, ^{14}_{7}N + \, ^{0}_{-1}e$

3) GAMMA EMISSION:
A γ-ray is a <u>photon</u> with no mass and no charge: $^{0}_{0}\gamma$

After an <u>alpha or beta emission</u> the nucleus sometimes has <u>extra energy to get rid of</u>. It does this by emitting a <u>gamma ray</u>. Gamma emission <u>never changes</u> the <u>atomic or mass numbers</u> of the nucleus.

A typical combined α- and γ-emission: $^{238}_{92}U \rightarrow \, ^{234}_{90}Th + \, ^{4}_{2}He + \, ^{0}_{0}\gamma$

The Radioactivity of a Sample Always Decreases Over Time

1) This is <u>pretty obvious</u> when you think about it. Each time a <u>decay</u> happens and an alpha, beta or gamma is given out, it means one more <u>radioactive nucleus</u> has <u>disappeared</u>.

2) Obviously, as the <u>unstable nuclei</u> all steadily disappear, the <u>activity as a whole</u> will also <u>decrease</u>. So the <u>older</u> a sample becomes, the <u>less radiation</u> it will emit.

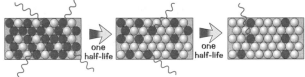

3) <u>How quickly</u> the activity <u>drops off</u> varies a lot. For <u>some</u> it takes <u>just a few hours</u> before nearly all the unstable nuclei have <u>decayed</u>, whilst others last for <u>millions of years</u>.

4) The problem with trying to <u>measure</u> this is that <u>the activity never reaches zero</u>, which is why we have to use the idea of <u>half-life</u> to measure how quickly the activity <u>drops off</u>.

5) Learn this <u>important definition</u> of <u>half-life</u>: Another definition of half-life is: "<u>The time taken for the activity (or count rate) to fall by half</u>". Use either.

> <u>HALF-LIFE</u> is the <u>TIME TAKEN</u> for <u>HALF</u> of the radioactive atoms now present to <u>DECAY</u>

6) A <u>short half-life</u> means the <u>activity falls quickly</u>, because <u>lots</u> of the nuclei decay <u>quickly</u>.

7) A <u>long half-life</u> means the activity <u>falls more slowly</u> because <u>most</u> of the nuclei don't decay <u>for a long time</u> — they just sit there, <u>basically unstable</u>, but kind of <u>biding their time</u>.

Do Half-Life Questions Step By Step

Half-life is maybe a little confusing, but Exam calculations are <u>straightforward</u> so long as you do them slowly, <u>STEP BY STEP</u>. Like this one:

<u>A VERY SIMPLE EXAMPLE</u>: The activity of a radio-isotope is 640cpm (counts per minute). Two hours later it has fallen to 40 cpm. Find the half life of the sample.

<u>ANSWER</u>: You must go through it in <u>short simple steps</u> like this:

INITIAL count:		after ONE half-life:		after TWO half-lives:		after THREE half-lives:		after FOUR half-lives:
640	$(\div 2)\rightarrow$	320	$(\div 2)\rightarrow$	160	$(\div 2)\rightarrow$	80	$(\div 2)\rightarrow$	40

Notice the careful <u>step by step method</u>, which tells us it takes <u>four half-lives</u> for the activity to fall from 640 to 40. Hence <u>two hours</u> represents four half-lives so the <u>half-life is 30 minutes</u>.

Half-life Calculations: Step by Step

Measuring The Half-life of a Sample Using a Graph

1) This can only be done by taking several readings of count rate using a G-M tube and counter.
2) The results can then be plotted as a graph, which will always be shaped like the one below.
3) The half-life is found from the graph, by finding the time interval on the bottom axis corresponding to a halving of the activity on the vertical axis. Easy peasy really.

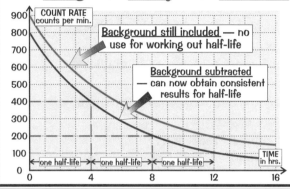

One trick you need to know is about the background radiation, which also enters the G-M tube and gives false readings. Measure the background count first and then subtract it from every reading you get, before plotting the results on the graph. Realistically, the only difficult bit is actually remembering about that for your Exam, should they ask you about it. They could also test that idea in a calculation question.

Carbon-14 Calculations — or Radio-Carbon Dating

Carbon-14 makes up about 1/10 000 000 (One ten-millionth) of the carbon in the air. This level stays fairly constant in the atmosphere. The same proportion of C-14 is also found in living things. However, when they die, the C-14 is trapped inside the wood or wool or whatever, and it gradually decays with a half-life of 5,600 years. By simply measuring the proportion of C-14 found in some old axe handle, burial shroud, etc. you can easily calculate how long ago the item was living material using the known half-life.

EXAMPLE: An axe handle was found to contain 1 part in 40 000 000 Carbon-14. How old is the axe?
ANSWER: The C-14 was originally 1 part in 10 000 000. After one half-life it would be down to 1 part in 20 000 000. After two half-lives it would be down to 1 part in 40 000 000. Hence the axe handle is two C-14 half-lives old, i.e. 2 × 5,600 = 11,200 years old.
Note the same old stepwise method, going down one half-life at a time.

There are lots of half-life questions in Physics — The Formula Bits.

Relative Proportions Calculations — Easy, As Long As You Learn It

Uranium isotopes have a very long half-life and decay via a series of short-lived particles to produce stable isotopes of lead. The relative proportions of uranium and lead isotopes in a sample of igneous rock can therefore be used to date the rock, using the known half-life of the Uranium. It's as simple as this:

Initially	After one half-life	After two half-lives	After three half-lives
100% Uranium	50% Uranium	25% Uranium	12.5% Uranium
0% lead	50% lead	75% lead	87.5% lead

Ratio of Uranium to lead: (half-life of Uranium-238 = 4.5 billion years)

Initially	After one half-life	After two half-lives	After three half-lives
1:0	1:1	1:3	1:7

Similarly, the proportions of potassium-40 and its stable decay product argon-40 can also be used to date igneous rocks, so long as the argon gas hasn't been able to escape. The relative proportions will be exactly the same as for the uranium and lead example above. Learn these ratios:

Initially	After one half-life	After two half-lives	After three half-lives
100% : 0%	50% : 50%	25% : 75%	12.5% : 87.5%
1:0	1:1	1:3	1:7

Learn about Half-life — and get things in proportion...

These half-life calculations are really pretty simple. Try these:
1) An isotope has a half-life of 12 mins. How long will it take to drop from 840cpm to 210cpm?
2) A sample of rock contains Uranium and lead in the ratio 75:525. How old is the rock?

Revision Summary for Section Six

It's an outrage — just so much stuff you've gotta learn — it's all work, work, work, no time to rest, no time to play. But then that's the grim, cruel reality of life in 21st century Britain — just drudgery, hard work and untold weariness... "And then he woke up and it had all been a dream..." Yeah, maybe life's not so bad after all — even for hard-done-by teenagers. Just a few jolly bits and bobs to learn in warm, cosy, comfortable civilisation. Practise these questions over and over again till you can answer them ALL effortlessly. Smile and enjoy. ☺

1) Sketch an atom. Give three details about the nucleus and the electrons.
2) Draw up a table detailing the mass and charge of the three basic subatomic particles.
3) Explain what the mass number and atomic number of an atom represent.
4) Explain what isotopes are. Give an example. Are most isotopes stable or unstable?
5) What was the Plum Pudding Model? Who put paid to that crazy old idea?
6) Describe Rutherford's Scattering Experiment with a diagram and say what happened.
7) What was the inevitable conclusion to be drawn from this experiment?
8) What is the main difference between EM radiation and nuclear radiation?
9) Describe in detail the nature and properties of the three types of radiation: α, β, and γ.
10) How do the three types compare in penetrating power and ionising power?
11) List several things which will block each of the three types.
12) Radioactive decay is a totally random process. Explain what this means.
13) Will anything cause a nucleus to undergo radioactive decay? What about nuclear fission?
14) Sketch a fairly accurate pie chart to show the six main sources of background radiation.
15) List three places where the level of background radiation is increased and explain why.
16) Describe in detail how radioactive isotopes are used in each of the following:
    a) tracers in medicine   b) tracers in industry   c) sterilisation   d) thickness control
    e) treating cancer   f) dating of rock samples   g) generating power.
17) Draw a labelled diagram of a Geiger-Müller tube and explain what it's for and how it works.
18) What units is radioactivity measured in? How many of those units are equal to 120cpm?
19) What are the two common methods of detecting radioactivity? Which is the simplest?
20) How is photographic film used in little badges to monitor radiation?
21) Write down the nuclear equation for the alpha decay of   a) $^{234}_{92}U$ b) $^{230}_{90}Th$ and c) $^{226}_{88}Ra$.
22) Write down the nuclear equation for the beta/gamma decay of a) $^{234}_{90}Th$ b) $^{234}_{91}Pa$ and c) $^{14}_{6}C$.
23) Sketch a diagram to show how the activity of a sample keeps halving.
24) Give a proper definition of half-life. How long and how short can half-lives be?
25) Sketch a typical graph of activity against time. Show how the half-life can be found.
26) What's the single most important thing to remember when doing half-life calculations?
27) An old bit of cloth was found to have 1 atom of C-14 to 80,000,000 atoms of C-12.
    Using the information on P. 89, calculate the age of the bit of cloth.
28) A rock contains Uranium-238 atoms and stable lead atoms in the ratio 1:3.
    If the half-life of Uranium-238 is 4.5×10^9 years, how old is the rock?
29) Exactly what kind of damage does radiation do inside body cells?
30) What damage do low doses cause? What effects do higher doses have?
31) Which kind of sources are most dangerous a) inside the body   b) outside the body?
32) List four safety precautions for the school lab., and three more for nuclear workers.

Answers
P.20 **Revn Sumy** **19) a)** 0.125A   **b)** 240C   **c)** 321W   **d)** 14Ω
P.32 **Revn Sumy** **11)** 7.5m/s^2 **12)** 5.7kg   **16)** 0.09m/s, 137m   **19)** 35m/s^2 **34)** 3120cm^3 **P.37** **1)** 330m/s
2) 200kHz   **P.38 1)** 264 m   **2)** 490 m   **P.53 Revn Sumy** **12) a)** 500,000 Hz   **b)** 0.35m   **c)** 4,600,000 Hz
d) 0.04m/s **e)** 150s   **13)** 150m/s   **14)** 5×10^{-6}s   **15)** 1980m   **16)** 0.86s   **P.80** **Revn Sumy** **8)** 6420 J   **10)**
2000 W, 1700 W   **11)** 20,631 J   **12)** 945 W **13)** 20 m/s   **14)** 10%   **P.89 1)** 24 mins   **2)** 13.5 billion years **P.90**
21) a) $^{234}_{92}U \rightarrow ^{230}_{90}Th + ^4_2He$ **b)** $^{230}_{90}Th \rightarrow ^{226}_{88}Ra + ^4_2He$ **c)** $^{226}_{88}Ra \rightarrow ^{222}_{86}Rn + ^4_2He$ **2) a)** $^{234}_{90}Th \rightarrow ^{234}_{91}Pa + ^0_{-1}e + ^0_0\gamma$
b) $^{234}_{91}Pa \rightarrow ^{234}_{92}U + ^0_{-1}e + ^0_0\gamma$ **c)** $^{14}_6C \rightarrow ^{14}_7N + ^0_{-1}e + ^0_0\gamma$ **27)** 16,800 yrs   **28)** 9×10^9 yrs

Index

Index